Studymates

25 Key Topics in Business Studies
25 Key Topics in Human Resources
25 Key Topics in Marketing
Accident & Emergency Nursing
Business Organisation
Cultural Studies
English Legal System
European Reformation
GCSE Chemistry
GCSE English
GCSE History: Schools History Project
GCSE Sciences
Genetics
Land Law
Macroeconomics
Memory
Organic Chemistry
Practical Drama & Theatre Arts
Revolutionary Conflicts
Social Anthropology
Social Statistics
Speaking Better French
Speaking English
Studying Chaucer
Studying History
Studying Literature
Studying Poetry
Studying Psychology
Understanding Maths
Using Information Technology

Many other titles in preparation

Memory

**What it is and how it works:
facts, theories and approaches**

Dr Peter Marshall

Studymates

First published in 2002 by Studymates Limited, PO Box 2, Taunton, Somerset TA3 3YE

Telephone:	(01823) 432002
Fax:	(01823) 430097
Series web site:	http://www.studymates.co.uk

Typeset by PDQ Typesetting, Newcastle-under-Lyme, Staffordshire.
Printed and bound in Great Britain, by Bell & Bain Ltd.

Contents

List of Illustrations and Tables

List of illustrations

List of tables

Preface

Most people have heard the saying, *'We are what we eat.'* I have a better saying: *'We are our memories.'*

What we have stored in our heads over the course of our lives can account for what we have become – our personality, our level of achievement, and much, much more. It can even explain our illnesses where they have a psychological aspect and this is often the case. Memories account for our knowledge and can in part account for our level of ability. There are genetic and other biological factors to take into account, but they only determine potential. What we make of it, how we unfold and realise it, that is the role of learning. The memories are not always of the explicit kind; much of our learning is unconscious, as the mind registers what leads to pleasure and what leads to pain, making us, as the old proverb says: *'Once bitten, twice shy.'*

Research, by myself and my colleagues at London University, has found that memory quality has now replaced IQ as the dominant predictor of school outcomes. Therefore the more we know about how to use memory to its full advantage, the more we can help children to achieve their full potential in education. If the nature of memory is understood, we can enhance our ability to use it in ways that will maximise its potential. We can also override negative effects of unconscious memories, if we can recognise them.

A great deal is now known about the process, from molecule to recall, but there is still a lot to be discovered.

This book explores:

▶ how memory works physiologically and chemically

▶ how it develops by conditioning and training

▶ how it sometimes plays tricks on us to protect us

▶ how it can fail through physiological damage and how we can overcome this situation.

I am delighted to be part of the growing Studymates list and I hope teachers, students and lecturers will recommend this book to others, and use it to further their own understanding of the whole nature of memory.

Peter Marshall
Newport
South Wales
peter.marshall@studymates.co.uk

1

The Cognitive Psychology of Memory

One-minute summary: This chapter will introduce you to the concepts involved in studying memory. You will be introduced to the **dual process model**, which treats **long** and **short-term memory** as two separate systems. The chapter will also discuss the **level of processing model**. This model assumes that long and short-term memory are not two systems. **Schemata theory** will be used to explain memory as the mapping of experience onto the brain, in the form of permanently modified neural pathways. The structure of long-term and short-term memory will also be discussed and we will look at what kind of things we remember best. Finally the chapter will look at the process of forgetting.

This chapter will help you to understand:

▶ the main contributions to memory knowledge which have come from cognitive psychology
▶ the relevance of studying memory from a cognitive perspective
▶ the main concerns of cognitive psychologists in respect of memory.

A fundamental divergence in the writings on the cognitive psychology of memory is, whether short-term memory and long-term memory are different processes?

The dual process model

The view that short-term memory and long-term memory are different processes is embodied in Atkinson and Shiffrin's[1] dual process model. It posits that information comes into the short-term memory via the sensory organs. If it is processed in some way it is transferred to long-term memory, where it can remain for life.

Otherwise it is lost from short-term memory within 15–30 seconds.

Evidence of relatively separate systems

People with brain damage provide a source of evidence that long and short-term memory are relatively separate systems. When accident or disease has caused damage to a region of brain structures known as the **limbic system** – particularly the structure known as the **hippocampus**, patients suffer an inability to store new information in long-term memory.

What is already there seems unaffected, as does their short-term memory. It is merely the process of transference from short-term memory to long-term memory which is affected. It is believed that the mechanism for consolidating long-term memories has been impaired in these cases.

Laboratory experiments

Another source of evidence that supports the idea of two relatively separate memory systems comes from laboratory experiments on serial reproduction patterns. When subjects have been given a list of words to recall, they have been found to remember more from the beginning and end of the list than from the middle. This is known as the serial reproduction effect. It appears, therefore, that the items they were recalling were coming from different memory systems. Those recalled from the first part of the list were coming from long-term memory and those from the last part were coming from short-term memory. If there were just one memory system, rather than two, the items they recalled would be expected to have been pretty uniformly distributed throughout the list.

Additional evidence comes from the fact that what people recall after a long period of time differs in the way it has been encoded from what people recall after only a short period. When people are asked to recall words after only a short duration, the errors they make tend to be errors of similar sound. This suggests that they encode the data acoustically. Errors in recall after a long period tend to be errors of semantics, i.e. of meaning.

Weaknesses of the dual-process model

It has been argued that the two-process model of memory is too simple. Different kinds of long-term memory have, after all, been identified, e.g. **episodic and procedural memory**.

The level of processing model

The alternative view is embodied in Craik and Lockhart's[2] level of processing model. This posits that rather than two separate stores there is only one. It is the depth to which the information is processed that determines whether or not it will remain. The more information is processed the stronger the memory trace will be and, therefore, the more enduring the memory.

Evidence for the level of processing model

Craik and Tulvin[3] demonstrated this model. They showed subjects a number of words and induced them to process them to different depths. Some they asked whether the words were written in capital letters or not. A second group was asked whether they rhymed with other words. A third group was asked if the words would fit into a particular sentence where there was a blank. They found the words which had been considered in terms of rhyme (acoustic processing) were remembered more than the words which had been considered in terms of appearance (visual processing). A greater proportion still was recalled of those that had been considered in terms of their appropriateness in a particular sentence (semantic processing).

Weaknesses of the level of processing model

This model has even more weaknesses than the dual processing model.

- ▶ It is too simple.[4]

- ▶ There is evidence that minimum, but meaningful, elaboration can be more effective than multiple, but less meaningful, elaboration.[5]

- ▶ It is difficult to measure the depth to which data has been processed.[6]

The evidence for the dual process model outweighs that for the level of processing model and most psychologists now accept the former.

Long-term memory

When investigating long-term memory, cognitive psychologists are interested in:

► its content and structure
► the codes it uses
► how we can make the best of it.

Let's deal with content and structure first. This will involve looking at:

► the form in which long-term memory appears to hold data.
► the categories of data that appear in long-term memory.
► the way these categories are structured.

The form in which long-term memory appears to hold data

Schemata theory
Long-term memory appears to hold data in the form of **schemata**.[7] Schemata are configurations of permanently modified neural pathways as a result of experience. They are mappings of experience onto the cerebrum – mappings of our interactions with the external world. As a result of them, we can recall and relive an experience after it has happened.

Schemata become interconnected, so that we can make connections between different facts and experiences.

Slots in schemata
Schemata have slots in which we can change one bit of data for another.[8] We can, for example, put ourselves in the place of someone else in a particular stored event. This enables us to make predictions about the consequences of behaving in a particular way.

We have schemata representing various levels of abstraction,[8] for example:

► family
► local community
► society.

At even higher levels of abstraction, we have schemata for our understanding of purely abstract concepts, like power, freedom, love, success and so on. Our schemata give us our cultural understanding.

Weaknesses of schemata theory
Schemata theory has been criticised on the following grounds:

► It is too vague.

► It doesn't account for reports of very precise memories.

► It is subject to the *chicken and egg paradox*. Understanding depends on schemata and schemata depend on understanding.

According to Piaget, however, it is schemata that develops first, from early psychomotor responses.[9]

What kinds of things are stored in long-term memory?
Our long-term memory holds data of many kinds:

► facts	► theories	► techniques
► experiences	► ideas	► aims
► assumptions	► concepts	► objectives
► beliefs	► feelings	► dictionary
► opinions	► rules of grammar	► thesaurus
► values	► strategies	► models
► algorithms		

Two relatively separate parts of long-term memory have been identified:[10]

▶ episodic memory (EM)
▶ semantic memory (SM).

Episodic memory

Episodic memory appears to hold autobiographical data, including:

▶ time
▶ place
▶ experience.

Semantic memory

Semantic memory contains such things as:

▶ concepts
▶ facts
▶ language
▶ rules.

Semantic memory is, inevitably, more structured than episodic memory and, thus, more stable and retrievable. In the latter, we tend to simply take and store experience as it comes to us in its rather random fashion. Consequently, episodic memory can be expected to be affected more by interference.

Interaction between the two is inevitable. The data held in semantic memory assists in perception and comprehension of subjective experience and the data held in autobiographical memory feeds the store in semantic memory.

Structure of semantic memory

It used to be thought that semantic memory is organised hierarchically in terms of common features. For example, a duck would be stored as an animal, subcategorised as a bird and further subcategorised as one of the aquatic kind. It was believed to be the case because hierarchical structures tend to be more efficient than non-hierarchical ones. Evidence, too, seemed to point to this. Question response times tend to be a function of the number of levels of the hierarchy the respondent has to move between.

Weakness of the hierarchical model
This evidence could, however, be explained in another way. The further down the assumed hierarchy something would lie, the greater the overall category size to which it belonged would be. It could be this that is related to, and explains, the difference in response times.

There are other weaknesses, too. Level of familiarity with a concept sometimes appears, to some degree, to be more important than its position in the hierarchy.

The non-hierarchical model
Semantic memory is now believed to be non-hierarchical.[11] Distance between stored concepts represents how readily associations will be made between them. There are various kinds of link that may be made between concepts. These include:

____	*is a*	____
____	*is not a*	____
____	*can*	____
____	*cannot*	____
____	*has*	____
____	*has not*	____

Codes and cues
Long-term memory appears to employ largely semantic coding. This is coding according to meaning. There are reasons, however, to believe this is not the only coding system employed.[12] After all, we remember tunes and we remember faces that we have only seen once for an instant. When we recall emotionally charged events we experience the feeling we felt at the time and particular smells are often recognised after many years have passed since the initial exposure.

Cued recall is recall aided by cues encoded with the data. These amount to other data intentionally, or unintentionally, stored at the same time. **Cues** can be:

▶ internal *(e.g. state of mind)*
▶ external *(e.g. context)*.

Mood congruency

When your conditions of life are positive and everything is going well you will feel happy. Consequently, in the future, when you feel happy, you will remember the things that went well for you in the past. Conversely, when times are difficult, you are likely to be unhappy. In the future, when you are unhappy, you will be more likely to remember the bad experiences.[13] This is because the bad feelings were stored along with the bad memories just as the good feelings were stored along with the good memories.

Situational cues

If you store material in a particular context you may recall it better in the same context than in a different one.[14] Differences of context can reduce recall potential[15] by as much as 30 per cent.

Context is only important in situations where recall is required.[16] Where it is recognition of material that is called for, context does not seem to have a significant effect. Presumably this is because the effect of the recognition cues deliberately given compensates for the lack of situational cues.

Sometimes cues are deliberately presented by others, e.g. when a child fails to thank a person who gives it a present its parent may say, 'What do you say?' Multiple-choice questions in exams and cloze tests are other examples. The latter are sentences with a word blanked out. Pupils have to select the term that will fit. They are commonly used in language teaching.

Sometimes people fail to remember something despite being given numerous cues. This is because the cues given may not be those which have been encoded with the data in long-term memory.

Timing

Does it matter when the cues are put in? There is disagreement on this. Tulvin[17] argued that if cues are to work they must be encoded into material at the time of storage.

However, this view is not held by all of the authorities.

Short-term memory

Short-term memory is sometimes referred to as working memory, because it holds data while it is being processed.[18] It is believed to have four components:[19]

▶ **articulatory (or phonological) loop**

▶ **primary acoustic store**

▶ **visuo-spatial scratchpad (or sketchpad)**

▶ **central executive.**

The function of short-term memory

It has been argued that its function is mainly storage while that of long-term memory is retrieval. Short-term memory either transfers things to long-term memory, or loses them as the trace decays. Long-term memory makes information available as and when needed, like a library.

The articulatory loop
The articulatory loop is sited in the inner ear. It is a sort of inner voice, a verbal rehearsal mechanism for auditory information. This part of the short-term memory is active, for example, when we repeat phone numbers to ourselves.

The primary acoustic store
The primary acoustic store has a limited capacity for storing auditory information. Information reaches it directly, through the ears, from the original source (e.g. a person speaking to us), or from the echo in the articulatory loop.

The visuo-spatial scratchpad (or sketchpad)
The visuo-spatial scratchpad does not have a primary store to transfer information to. Instead, visual information has to be converted to phonological code and then fed to the primary acoustic store via the articulatory loop.

The central executive

The central executive controls the allocation of resources to each part of the mechanism. It is modality-free, so different kinds of sensory data can be dealt with simultaneously.

The articulatory loop and visuo-spatial scratchpad are not modality-free, i.e. their function is limited to a particular sense. The articulatory loop functions only with auditory data and the visio-spatial scratchpad with visual data. This means that subsequent data of the same modality will displace data presently in either of these parts.

Since the central executive is modality-free, different auditory and visual data can be dealt with simultaneously. In practice, we know this to be the case, since we can drive a car while talking to our passenger about something entirely different to the road ahead.

Sensory memory and the multi-store model

Atkinson and Shiffrin, who identified separate long and short-term memory processes, also identified a third memory component – **sensory memory**. This is not a memory system in quite the same way as the others. Short-term memory and long-term memory essentially involve coding of data. Sensory memory does not; it merely holds it in its original sensory form. However, some prefer to regard all three systems as parts of memory. They therefore refer to Atkinson and Shiffrin's model not as the dual process model, but as the **multi-store model**.

Relationship between memory, attention and perception

There are overlaps between the subjects of memory, attention and perception. The multi-store model of memory and Broadbent's model of attention have sensory memory as a common component. Broadbent had posited the existence of a sensory memory, or sensory buffer store, ten years before Atkinson and Shiffrin published their model. He identified it as an essential part of the attentional process.

There is a similarly conspicuous connection between memory and perception. Atkinson and Shiffrin described the way data pass from sensory memory to short-term memory. The data are scanned for a pattern match with data held in long-term memory. If a match is found the data passes to short-term memory. The process of pattern recognition is, arguably, the essence of perception itself. Perception is the link between sensory memory and short-term memory. It also follows from what has been said that it has a direct link with long-term memory. A case can therefore be made for concluding that neither memory, attention, nor perception can be studied in isolation from each other.

Recent models

Paivio posited a short-term memory mechanism which involves a verbal and a non-verbal component.[20] For example, if you are processing the visual image of a house, you will, on some level, be counting the visible windows and noting the different colours – all phonological processes.

The verbal component converts data into signals that he refers to as **logogens** and the non-verbal converts visual data into **imagens**. **Referential links** are made between each component. The imagens of the visual data connect with their corresponding logogens and vice versa.

Types of memory

▶ **Echoic memory** lasts only about two seconds.

▶ **Eidetic memory** is what is often referred to as a photographic memory. The term comes from the Greek term *eidos*, which means *that which is seen.*

▶ **Flash-bulb memory** is a type of episodic memory. It is where a situation is strongly imprinted in the memory because it is highly emotionally charged. This emotional charge of flash-bulb memory has been challenged. Neisser [21] argued that the strong imprinting could be the result of rehearsal and reconsideration.

▶ **Iconic memory** is of the shortest duration. It lasts only about half a second.

MEMORY TYPES

▶ long-term memory *(long-term storage)*

▶ short-term memory *(working memory)*

▶ autobiographical, episodic memory *(passive storage of experience)*

▶ experimental, episodic memory *(deliberate storage of data)*

▶ declarative memory *(storage of knowledge)*

▶ procedural memory *(storage of skills)*

▶ echoic memory *(acoustic storage of very short duration)*

▶ flashbulb memory *(storage enhanced in detail by emotional charge)*

▶ iconic memory *(extremely short-term retention)*

▶ eidetic memory *(the capacity to retain vivid accurate and enduring after-images of visual perceptions)*

▶ semantic memory *(storage of things like concepts, facts rules and words)*

▶ reconstructive memory *(mixture of true and unwittingly made up memories)*

▶ cue-dependent memory *(recall dependent on cues)*

▶ context dependent memory *(recall dependent on settting)*

▶ state dependent memory *(recall dependent on state of mind)*

What kind of things can we remember best?

We remember things best if they are:

▶ positive

▶ concrete rather then abstract

▶ interacting (pairs of words are better than single words)

▶ bizarre, as opposed to ordinary

▶ pictures (better than words)

▶ general themes, as opposed to detail

▶ elaborate as opposed to plain.

The reason we can recall more concrete ideas better than relatively abstract ones is that they evoke mental images more readily.

How pairing helps
Imagining interacting pairs of images may work better because one provides an inbuilt cue for the other. The image also becomes more dynamic than would be the case for either of the words separately.

Why bizarre images are remembered easily
The bizarreness of the image may have its effect because its distinctiveness protects it from interference from other ideas and knowledge. Its novelty value may also result in a deeper level of processing.

Why pictures are easier to remember
The reason pictures are easier to recall than words is that the visual processing of the picture evokes an auditory image too, both at storage and at recall stages.

Why general themes are easier to remember
The reason general themes are easier to remember than detail

could be that the relative frequency of feature occurrence translates into a corresponding relative depth of processing. General themes may also be easier to perceive in the first place than a mass of individual details.

Elaboration and retention
Craik and Tulvin[3] assumed that retention is positively related to degree of elaboration. This has been challenged, however. Evidence was produced that minimum, but meaningful elaboration can be more effective than multiple, but less meaningful elaboration.[5]

Positiveness and accuracy
Accuracy seems better when recollection is positive, i.e. people can more accurately remember when something did happen than when something didn't.

Retention qualities in order of importance
Eysenck[22] suggested that distinctiveness, elaboration and level of processing influence long-term storage, in that order of importance.

Incidental storage
Besides what we intend to store we also store incidental things. This is inevitable, since we do not have conscious control over what we perceive.

Forgetting

There are various reasons why we forget things. They include:

▶ **trace decay**
▶ **displacement**
▶ **retroactive interference**
▶ **pro-active interference**
▶ **prevention of consolidation**
▶ **motivated forgetting, of various types.**

Trace decay and its effects

Is trace decay a major cause of forgetting? If it were, people would be able to remember a rapidly presented series of digits better than a similar series presented more slowly. It is assumed that trace decay is a function of time. The shorter the space of time between the presentation of each digit the less time there would be for such trace decay to occur. The evidence is ambiguous. Shallice[23] found that rapidly presented digits were recalled more easily than those presented slowly. Waugh and Norman,[24] however, produced evidence that this was not the case.

Displacement and interference by other memories appear to be the most important sources of forgetting.

Displacement

Displacement affects short-term memory. What we can hold in this memory store at any one time is severely limited. New features attended to of the same modality (e.g. acoustic, or visual) will displace data already there.

Interference

Interference provides an explanation for why forgetting increases with time. The longer the time span since the material was stored, the greater the number of competing memories there will be.

Internal and external sources of interference

Interference can come from:

▶ internal sources *material already stored in memory*
▶ external sources *data present in one's perceptual set.*

Retroactive and pro-active interference

Interference can affect:

▶ what is presently stored *retroactive interference*
▶ what is yet to be stored *proactive interference.*

What is retroactive interference?

Retroactive interference is where memory is obscured, or polluted by data stored subsequently.

The effect of retroactive interference is demonstrated by the fact that less tends to be forgotten during sleep than during waking hours. If you store material just before going to sleep, you are more likely to be able to recall it on waking than you would eight hours or so later if you had not been to sleep in the meantime. This kind of interference appears to decrease over time.

What is pro-active interference?

Proactive interference is where memories are obscured, or polluted by material stored earlier. It appears to increase with time.[25] This is understandable, since the amount of material stored and available as a source of interference also grows over time.

Code similarity of material is an important source of interference in short-term memory e.g. new visual material will interfere with other visual material in short-term memory but not with verbal material, and vice-versa. It does not seem to apply to long-term memory. There the dominant code is semantic, ie conversion of the sensory material to reasoned propositions, and semantic similarity does not seem to cause forgetting.

The weakness of interference theory

A weakness of interference theory is that the data on which it is based has been produced in laboratories. It is not known to what degree it can be generalised to situations outside them. We would, therefore, describe the theory as having *low external validity*.

Eye-witness testimony and retroactive interference

Retroactive interference has important consequences for eye-witness testimony in court proceedings. It has been argued that the form of questions used can influence witnesses in their reconstruction of events. This is an example of an external source of retroactive interference. For example, using 'the' instead of 'a' can lead the witness to interpret things more positively, though this may mean less accurately. The choice of action verbs is another example. Asking somebody what speed a car was doing when it *bumped* another car is likely to elicit a different response than if you asked them what speed it was doing when it *crashed* into the other car.[26] Asking the second form of the question is likely to elicit a report of faster speed than the first. Such questions are referred to as leading questions, for they lead a person in respect of how to interpret what they are recalling. They are likely to have the greatest effect where:

▶ the witness is not expecting to be misled
▶ there has been a significant lapse of time since the event.[27]

Eye-witness testimony, therefore, is not a sound ground for conviction in court. It is only safe to consider it as corroborative evidence, along with other sources.

Tutorial

Seminar discussion
How useful is the cognitive approach to memory? What questions can it give us answers to and what questions can it not?

Student assignment
Ask half a dozen people to do their best to learn a list of 20 words in four minutes. A suitable list can be downloaded from *www.thememorysite.co.uk*. Test their recall. Consider whether the data demonstrates the serial reproduction effect (see page 12).

Practice questions
1. What is the difference between the dual process model of memory and the level of processing model? *(Tick appropriate box)*

   The codes used   ☐
   The depth to which memory is processed   ☐
   The number of relatively different parts   ☐

2. State four weaknesses of the level of processing model.

3. Which is the more structured? *(Tick appropriate box)*

   semantic memory   ☐
   episodic memory   ☐

4. Which four of the following kinds of images would be remembered best and which four would be remembered least?

sensible images	visual images
humorous images	negative images
positive images	elaborate images
simple images	three-dimensional images

5. What are schemata? Tick which one of the following answers applies:

natural logic structures ☐
mental mappings of experience ☐
personal plans, or designs ☐

6. How many bits of information can short-term memory hold? Tick which one of the following answers applies:

between 5 and 7 ☐
7 ☐
between 5 and 9 ☐

Bibliographical notes

1 Atkinson and Shiffrin (1971)
2 Craik and Lockhart (1972)
3 Craik and Tulvin (1975)
4 Eysenck (1986)
5 Bransford *et al.* (1979), Jacoby and Craik (1979), Eysenck and Eysenck (1980)
6 Baddeley (1990), Bartlett (1932), Minsky (1975), Rumelhart (1975)
7 Bartlett (1932), Baddeley (1990), Misky (1975), Rumelhart (1975), Schank (1975)
8 Rumelhart and Norman (1983)
9 Piaget and Inhelder (1969)
10 Tulvin (1972)
11 Collins and Loftus (1975)
12 See Morris (1978)
13 Bower (1981)
14 Abernathy (1940)
15 Eich (1980), Baddeley (1975)
16 Baddeley (1996b)
17 Tulvin (1983)
18 Cohen (1990)
19 Salame and Baddeley (1982)
20 Pavio (1971)
21 Neisser (1982)
22 Eysenck (1979)
23 Shallice (1967)
24 Waugh and Norman (1965)
25 See Underwood (1957)
26 Loftus and Palmer (1974)
27 Cohen (1986)

2

The Behavioural Psychology of Memory

One-minute summary: Some of our memory processes work in an associative way, i.e. by forming links with other items in memory at the storage stage, and using such links at the recall stage. We also associate events which are not directly related. Events which occur closely in time become associated even if there is no logical connection. We generalise the association to similar events and objects. You can't undo memories, but you can inhibit them. When memories have not been recalled for some time they fade. Undesirable associations can accidentally be stored – phobias. Phobias can be removed by desensitisation. Behavioural reinforcement can be positive, or negative. Punishment is not as effective as reward. Events which are not directly related can act as secondary reinforcers. Punishment can serve as a reward. Shaping involves segmenting maladapted behaviour and changing each bit by reinforcement methods. Drive reduction reinforces behaviour.

This chapter will help you to understand

- ▶ what is known as the behaviourist perspective on memory
- ▶ how memory works in an associative way
- ▶ the nature of classical conditioning
- ▶ the process of generalisation
- ▶ phobias and desensitisation
- ▶ operant conditioning
- ▶ shaping behaviour.

Memory and association

Some of our reflex memory processes work in an associative way. The memory process associates one aspect of sensory experience with another aspect and the association is stored. Every time I put on my outdoor coat my dog jumps up and rushes to my side. That is because whenever I get ready to take her for a walk I tend to put on that outdoor coat. She has stored in her reflex memory the association between me putting on that outdoor coat and the anticipation of a walk. Every time she experiences the former she also experiences the latter and all the excitement that goes with it.

But more often than not she is wrong about it. I am going out, but not to take her for a walk. So she doesn't really have a sufficient reason to assume my donning of my overcoat means she is going to go for a walk. The reason she makes the mistake is because this 'not directly related' event has become associated with the event which is 'directly related' to her being taken for a walk – that event is me fetching her lead. That really is a reliable predictor; she has every reason to infer from that that she is going for a walk.

The visit to the dentist

Here is another example. Many people, if not most, are a little afraid of going to the dentist. Yet in most cases (though admittedly not all) dental treatment is, today, more or less painless. Part of the reason some people still become afraid is that past dentist treatments have been painful and, therefore, they have caused them to anticipate pain in future treatments. Anticipation of pain results in anxiety and, consequently, the association between anxiety, on the one hand, and waiting in the dentist's waiting room, on the other hand, has been stored in reflex memory. Every time one is experienced the other is invoked – waiting to be called by the dentist and anxiety.

It was Pavlov who first wrote about how two events can become associated in the reflex memory so that the occurrence of one will invoke a response to the other. Pavlov noticed that it was not only the sight of food that would make dogs start to salivate; they would salivate on hearing the clanging sound of food buckets. The sight of food is a logical reason to expect food, but clanging of buckets could mean many things. Nevertheless, because they occurred closely together in time, the dogs' reflex memories stored the association, so that whenever they heard the clang they started to salivate. To describe this we say that the clang of the bucket had become conditioned by the sight of food. Once this conditioning had taken place the clang of the bucket became sufficient to produce salivation even if it was empty – much like my outdoor coat is enough to excite my dog in anticipation of a walk, even when she is not going to get one.

Classical conditioning

This process of automatic storage of associations in the reflex memory is known as **classical conditioning**. It is the process by which we learn to respond automatically to different experiences and by which we learn new skills. It can be summarised as follows:

Stage one	UCS → UCR
Stage two	CS + UCS → UCR
Stage three	CS → CR

UCS = Unconditioned Stimulus, UCR = Unconditioned Response,
S = Conditioned Stimulus, CR = Conditioned Response.

Table 1. The three stages of classical conditioning.

In the first stage, both stimulus and response have a logical connection – the sight of food has an intrinsic power to stimulate salivation. By stage three, however, neither the stimulus nor the response is logically connected; the bucket clang's power to stimulate salivation does not depend upon the presence of food, nor the overcoat on the inevitability of a walk. By this stage, there is no logical reason for the stimuli to cause the responses they do. They have no intrinsic power to stimulate the response, so we say they are **conditioned**. They are referred to as a conditioned stimulus and a conditioned response, because they have been given a kind of artificial potential. For such an association to be conditioned the two variables have to occur more or less together in time, at least within fifteen seconds of each other. Within this limit there is room to vary. If the clang of the bucket comes before the sight of food it is known as **forward conditioning.** It can be the other way round and that is known as **backward conditioning.** If they occur at the same time it is known as **simultaneous conditioning**. Forward conditioning and simultaneous conditioning are the most effective, but you will often see backward conditioning being used in advertisements – the desirable experience and then the product.

Generalisation

Watson and little Albert

The same response occurs, though to a lesser degree, in the presence of anything resembling the conditioned stimulus. In a notorious experiment, J. D. Watson, the founder of the Behaviourist School of Psychology, conditioned an infant to be frightened of a rat.[1] He did this by presenting the rat in front of the child and making a loud and startling noise at the same time. Little Albert's reflex memory stored the association between the rat and a feeling of fear. But Watson then found that things resembling a rat would also produce fear, even a piece of cotton wool. It seems that the conditioning rises up the levels of the schema, albeit with decreasing effect. To put it another way, it permeates back into more general levels of the **declarative memory** structure (known as schemata) so that it attaches the same quality to any object of the same colour and texture.

Once these associations have been made can they ever be undone?

Yes, to some degree but you can't simply reverse the storage process. What you can do is deliberately store a contradictory association and this will have an inhibiting effect on the one that preceded it. This is sometimes referred to as an **associative inhibition.** Associative inhibitions can be achieved by forming new responses to old stimuli, or associating new stimuli with old responses. The more strongly the new memory is stored the more inhibiting will be the effect. This is known as desensitisation. It is what, presumably, J. D. Watson would have done with little Albert, to take away the fear of rats and anything resembling them, which he had induced for the sake of his research. Unfortunately, Albert's mother snatched him away once she learned of the unauthorised experiment on her son and there is no telling how he coped with his newfound fear thereafter.

Although you can't do anything directly to make it happen, the synaptic changes that have taken place to form new associative memories do reverse themselves to some degree. When associations are stored in long-term memory new synaptic terminals grow and the size of active zones in presynaptic membranes increases. When the new association is not activated for long periods, however, the number of terminals declines and the size of the active zones decreases.

Phobias and desensitisation

Accidental association
Many people have, at some time in their lives, accidentally stored associations which have afterwards given them trouble. We call these effects phobias. Arachnophobia, for example, develops in this way. Everyone has experienced frightening situations at some time or other in their childhoods, parents rowing, for example. Suppose a child's peripheral vision picked up the presence of a spider at the same time, somewhere on the wall of the room. They would have been unaware of it because it was outside their focal vision, but it would have been registered in their brain, nevertheless, and the association made – spiders and fear. Thereafter, every time they would see a spider their fear response would be triggered and they may never understand the real reason why. The same goes for most phobias.

Inducing inhibiting responses
In most cases phobias can easily be removed by the induction of an inhibiting response. The most common method seems to be systematic desensitisation. Over 40 sessions or so[2] a phobia sufferer is exposed to an increasing dosage of the object of their fear. It may begin with exposure to the written word *spider*, for many phobics cannot even hear the word without fear. This may be followed, in a later session, with the spoken word *spider*. The next stage could involve a picture of a cartoon spider and then the presence of a real, but tiny, money spider. The progression would carry on in this way until the individual could cope with the presence of a full

sized spider without a debilitating level of fear. The reason for the gradual increase in level of exposure is so that compensatory action can be taken to cancel out the fear felt at each stage. We are incapable of feeling two contradictory emotions at the same time, so if a feeling of relaxation and calm is induced by a stronger stimulus than the one which is invoking fear, the fear emotion will not be able to be felt. The steps must be small ones, so that it is possible to exceed the power of the fear stimulus with the contradictory one. The result is that in each session the individual stores associations between spiders and a feeling of calm. By the end of the course of desensitisation sessions the individual will have a conditioned response of calmness in relation to spiders, which contradicts and, therefore, inhibits, the previously stored fear response.

Hypnosis and desensitisation

If combined with hypnosis (which makes the mind more readily accept new experiences) this process can be speeded up.

Other methods
Two other methods of desensitisation work in a very different way. These are:

▶ **saturation**
▶ **implosion**.

These rely on the assumption that there is an absolute ceiling to the feeling of fear – once it is reached the fear cannot increase further. Fear requires energy – without energy it will fade away. Consequently, when fear reaches the maximum level of its intensity it will remain there only as long as the energy is there to feed it. From there on the level of fear felt must fall.

These methods of desensitisation bring the phobia sufferers straight to the maximum exposure to the phobic object, straight to the ceiling of their fear. As their energy depletes itself the level of fear subsides and, as it does so, each reduced level of fear becomes associated with the phobic object, inhibiting the one before it, until a level of calm acceptance is reached. Many inhibitory responses have been stored here, each inhibiting its more troublesome predecessor.

In saturation, the real phobic object is used, while in implosion the sufferer is encouraged to imagine the phobic object. The fact that the original, troublesome associations are still there, just inhibited, is borne out by the fact that the original phobic response can quickly return if something causes the inhibiting response to fail. For example if the individual allows themselves to feel fear in the presence of the phobic object. Desensitisation is not, therefore, the last work in phobia treatment; it has to be followed by life-long self-discipline, to maintain the adaptive response.

Operant conditioning

Operant conditioning refers to the learning process, which involves storage of associations between particular actions, on the one hand, and rewards, or punishments, on the other. It differs from classical conditioning in that this refers to involuntary behavioural responses cued by perceptions. Operant conditioning refers to behavioural forms, which are voluntary, uncued and motivated by anticipation of a reward. Here the conditioning starts with voluntary behaviour, while in classical conditioning it starts with perception. If a particular action is rewarded it will be repeated. So universally is this the case that it can be classed as a law rather than just a theory. It is known as **Thorndyke's Law of Effect**. It provides that what happens as a result of behaviour will influence subsequent behaviour. If the consequence is pleasurable the behaviour will be repeated; if it is unpleasurable it will not. The principle authority in operant conditioning theory is A. F. Skinner.

Tom (1948) argued that things were not altogether that straightforward though. He found that it is not learning that is dependent upon a reward, just the behavioural expression of that learning. His findings showed that unrewarded rats learnt to navigate a maze more or less as well as those whose progress was rewarded but their learning remained latent; they didn't demonstrate it until they were rewarded. This suggests that storage of a skill in the memory is not dependent upon *storage* of a related skill – reward association, but the actual *performance* of that skill is dependent on such association.

Shaping behaviour

Human behaviour is shaped by reinforcement and punishment.

Reinforcement
Reinforcement refers to any outcomes of behaviour which lead to them being repeated.

Positive reinforcement
If a particular action is rewarded, either by praise, or physical pleasure, it will be repeated.

Negative reinforcement
Action which avoids pain or discomfort will also be repeated. In this way we learn to duck, or put up our hands in defence if someone is about to strike us.

Secondary reinforcement
Just as classical conditioning is subject to generalisation so operant conditioning is subject to something similar – secondary reinforcement. While a hug will act as a primary reinforcer, a smile will act as a secondary reinforcer, for the latter tends to be present with the former.

Accidental reinforcement
Sometimes behaviour is accidentally reinforced. This is one explanation of superstition. Contextual details contiguous to the experience of good or bad fortune become associated in the reflex memory with the experience. Wherever they occur again in our perceptual field they may evoke the feelings that were experienced in that event.

Punishment
Punishment weakens stored behavioural programs, reducing the

likelihood of them being expressed. Suppose a child stole another's sweets and this action was initially rewarded by the pleasure of eating them. A *behaviour-reward* association will have been stored which will have predisposed the child to steal sweets from others in the future. However, the expression of the *behaviour-reward association* will be weakened if the parents find out and punishes the child for its action. A *behaviour-punishment association* will then be stored and this will inhibit the expression of the original *behaviour-reward association.*

Overall, however, punishment is not a very effective method of shaping behaviour, for it:

▶ only prevents behavioural forms; it does nothing to encourage new ones[3]

▶ only suppresses, rather than removes undesirable behaviours

▶ motivates people to find ways of avoiding punishment, without changing the undesirable behaviour which attracts it.

If punishment is to be used, it is best to combine it with reward.[4]

Punishment as a reward
Sometimes a curious thing happens and it complicates the picture just a little. If reward is the most desirable thing then what is the least desirable – punishment? No, it is indifference. The worst thing in the world to most people is being ignored. So if a child never receives praise, whatever is does, it will seek condemnation. It will be naughty just to gain attention. Punishment is the best reward it can achieve – it's better than being ignored.

The dominant shaping agent of human behaviour is negative reinforcement. The reason this is the more powerful is that it sets up an inhibition and this prevents us testing the limits for ourselves. If a child only received positive reinforcement it would try anything. With negative reinforcement the child develops inhibitions, which prevent it trying things. It does not get the chance to see exactly how unpleasant the consequences of particular behaviours will be, if at all.

Shaping programmes

Seriously maladapted behaviour is sometimes treated by segmenting the behaviour and encouraging change in appropriate bits. Each changed behavioural element is individually reinforced, by praise, or some more tangible reward. Anorexia nervosa is sometimes treated in this way.

Hull's drive reduction theory

Hull was interested in the nature of conditioning stimuli. He argued that the only stimuli involved in conditioning were reductions in homeostatic drives – food, thirst, sex, temperature, etc. Homeostasis is a balance in bodily conditions. When we are becoming dehydrated we seek fluids to restore the balance. When we are running out of energy we seek food. Hull argued that no learning will take place if there is not such an imbalance.

Hull's theory has been widely challenged on the basis that humans have non-homeostatic, or secondary drives – the need for confidence, affiliation and self-actualisation, for example. The theory was thus amended by others[5] so that it included secondary drives (sometimes referred to as acquired drives).

One of our major secondary drives, according to Mowrer, is an anxiety reduction drive. Many things can cause anxiety. The most original source of all, it has been argued, is the fear of separation from others, the fear of isolation. If a behavioural form reduces the feeling of anxiety it will repeated; if it increases it, it will not.[6] The kinds of things which reduce anxiety include financial stability, occupational success and social affiliation.

People are also driven by a need to feel they are competent and if a behaviour makes them feel competent it will be repeated.

Non-homeostatic drives are very different from homeostatic drives. They involve a quest for stimulation, while homeostatic drives involve a quest for satisfaction.

Things are not quite that straightforward, however. People appear to be driven to achieve an optimum level of arousal.[7] If a behaviour form arouses us too much, or too little, we will be less likely to repeat it than if it arouses us to a level in between the two. Too little or too much gives us boredom, or sensory overload and neither of these are rewarding.

Then there is the case of sex, which is a contradictory drive. Up to a point it is a case of the more you get the more you want. This is known as the hypersensitising principle. After a while, however, the hypersensitising principle goes into reverse and it's a case of the more you get the less interested you are. Eventually, it reverses again and goes the other way.

Tutorial

Seminar discussion
1. Consider the merits of the three methods of removing phobias. Which would you choose if you wanted to get rid of a phobia?

2. Consider the merits of punishment and reward. Which would you use mainly if you wanted to shape the behaviour of others?

3. To what extent is our learning due to homeostatic drives and to what extent is it due to secondary drives?

Student assignment
Teach your dog to fetch something for you by rewarding it each time it does. Continue until you have done four consecutive, successful trials.

Practice questions
1. Which one of the following is correct? Reflex memory only stores association between events which:

   a. are logically connected
   b. occur closely together in time
   c. are logically connected and occur closely together in time.

2. Which two of the following are correct? Reflex memories:

   a. can be erased with the right techniques
   b. can never be erased
   c. can be inhibited
   d. can never be inhibited
   e. can neither be erase, nor inhibited.

3. If we store an association between an object and a fear, we are likely to be frightened of things which resemble that object.

   Tick appropriate box   True ☐   False ☐

4. Which three of the following are correct?
   a. Punishment is more effective than reward in conditioning behaviour.
   b. Reward is more effective than punishment in conditioning behaviour.
   c. Punishment and reward is more effective than punishment alone.
   d. The principle means of conditioning in humans is negative reinforcement.
   e. The principle means of conditioning in humans is reward.

Bibliographical notes

1   Watson and Raynor (1920)
2   Jones (1924)
3   Eystes (1970)
4   Hull (1980)
5   Dolland and Miller (1950), Mowrer (1950)
6   Mowrer (1950)
7   Berlyne (1969), Arkes and Gaske (1977)

3

The Psychoanalysis of Memory

One-minute summary: Memory plays an important part in the development of the psyche. Failure to habituate results in **fixation**. Strong anxiety can cause an individual to regress to an earlier developmental stage. **Inhibition** is a stronger moral force than guilt. Undesirable memories are dealt with by **suppression**, displacement, **projection**, or **repression**. Repressed memories are involuntarily recalled, in re-coded form, often involving physical symptoms. Repression can be primary, or secondary. The power of repressed memories can be reduced by bringing them into consciousness. The **superego** is a moral memory store, containing negatively and positively reinforced behaviour images. The **ego** also consists partly of memory stores. The **adapted child** is a store of attention-seeking tactics.

This chapter will help you to understand:

▶ the subject of memory from a psychoanalytical perspective
▶ the psychoanalytical concepts which relate to memory
▶ the development of the moral memory store known as the superego
▶ the development of the mind known as the ego
▶ the stages of development of the psyche
▶ abnormal development and its consequences.

The subject of memory from a psychoanalytical perspective

Chapter 1 dealt with conscious storage and conscious recall. Chapter 2 dealt with unconscious storage and unconscious recall. This chapter deals with an interaction of the two − where the content of the conscious mind is stored in the unconscious and recalled into the conscious mind. The way it is recalled is interesting, for it is recoded so that it emerges in disguised form. This chapter will explain how and why memory sometimes works in this strange way.

The psychoanalytical concepts which relate to memory

Psychoanalysis is the psychological discipline that sees all mental behaviour in terms of its function in the defence of the ego, i.e. saving it from intolerable anxiety. This is the thinking mind that manages our conscious life. The ego comes into being as a result of the building of an unconscious memory store known as the superego. Its role is to mediate between the latter and the individual's natural impulses. The ego itself consists partly of memory stores. Let us begin with the new-born mind and trace its development to that of the mature adult, looking at the role memory has to play in this and the kinds of memory stores to which this vein of psychological development gives rise.

The id
The early infant's psyche is purely impulse-led and entirely self-seeking. That natural impulse-led life force is known as the **id**.

The superego
From the onset of life, however, its parents apply restraint to those impulses. Infants have no ability to judge, so they simply store those disciplined attitudes uncritically. These internalised, parental attitudes which in turn represent the common attitudes of the society in which the parent and child live, have a restraining effect on the gratification of the infant's id or desire.

The admonishment or punishment it receives, in response to forbidden or discouraged behaviour, or that which it sees others suffering for particular behaviours, leads to inhibitions and guilt. An inhibition is felt as a result of strong warnings against particular behaviours. Guilt results from punishments after such acts. The warnings and experiences of punishment are stored in a special, unconscious memory store known as the superego and are recalled and relived if and when such behaviour is performed or contemplated again. One of the strongest deterrents is the threat of ostracism. According to some psychoanalysts, ostracism, like any other form of separation, makes us relive to some degree our own birth trauma.

The nurturing parent
Not all of our parents' attitudes and reactions to our behaviour are negative. They encourage and praise some things. We store these, too, in the same unchallenged form as the negative reactions – the *don'ts*. The memory store in which the positive attitudes and reactions they display towards particular behaviours we perform and those we observe in their interactions with others is referred to as the **nurturing parent**.[1] The negative attitudes store is known as the **admonishing parent**.[1] These are the two parts of the **moral memory store** known as the superego.

The ego
The effects of the superego are unnatural to us. They restrain our natural impulses. It is necessary that they do, for that is the cost we must pay for the advantage of living in society. We must all agree to restrain our natural desires to some degree and leave some of our wants unfulfilled, for social life is a compromise. We have to give and take. Nevertheless, there is a psychological cost to the restraint and its form is *anxiety*. The more we restrain our natural impulses, the more anxiety we experience.

If we allowed our superego to continue to control us throughout our lives, in the total way it does in our first years of life, our lives would be unbearable, especially when the strong, sexual urges of adolescence and adulthood begin to effect us. Furthermore, our parents will not always be there to protect us in a world which will keep on slapping our other cheek every time we turn it, a world where fairness and give and take is not always guaranteed and social rights often have to be asserted to be honoured.

Consequently the infant has to begin to build an adult centre in its mind, a centre of personal responsibility. It must develop judgement, knowledge, values and beliefs. It must develop an ability to criticise what its parents and others are telling it and showing it by example. This part of the psyche is known as the ego.

The ego develops from all the knowledge, skills and beliefs that build up in the memory and it employs the intellect and creative powers. It is a totally rational part of the psyche.

The adapted child

There appears to be a part of us which develops from a combination of the id, on the one hand, and the knowledge and rational rules which make up the ego, on the other. This is an unconscious memory store of a special kind, known as the adapted child.[1] It develops to quite a significant level where a child has to struggle to elicit shows of love and approval from its parents and other authority figures. The child develops conditioned tactics for gaining attention. Unruly behaviour and persistent crying are examples of adapted child behaviour, for at least this attracts condemnation or punishment and even this is better than no attention at all.

The benefits tend to be short-term; they invariably have negative consequences in the long-term. Accident proneness, for example, is a typical adapted child strategy. Accidents attract shows of love and support in the short-term, but accident proneness has long-term consequences, which can result in ostracism and even death.

The justification for classing this memory store as separate from the ego is that the latter is rational but the adaptive child's behaviour is not. It is simply the result of conditioned responses.

Of course, we all try to attract attention at times – it is often essential. It is only when that part of the psyche is overdeveloped that it causes problems in adult life. The naughty child type may become a habitual rule-breaker, or even a petty criminal. In both cases it is the punishment that is the main motive for the behaviour.

Stages of development of the psyche

The development of the psyche has several stages:

▶ oral-incorporative stage
▶ oral-aggressive stage

▶ anal-expulsive stage
▶ anal-retentive stage
▶ phallic stage
▶ consolidation stage
▶ genital stage.

As the psyche develops towards maturity memory plays an important part in the process in two ways:

▶ conditioning
▶ habituation.

At each stage a child's primary source of physical pleasure changes, ending up with the source which will ensure the survival of the species – genitalia – their own and others. Sex becomes their principal motivating force.

In each phase a new kind of association is stored and this modifies the individual's behaviour pattern. Eventually, the child becomes habituated to the special rewards of each stage and while they still guide behaviour to some degree they cease to be the principal motivating force. The child then moves on to explore the new source of pleasure which the next stage on provides.

When an individual is fixated in a particular stage the behaviour reward association relating to that stage continues to have a profound influence upon their behaviour.

Oral incorporative stage
An infant's first source of pleasure is its mouth. It sucks its mother's nipple and receives food. It also sucks everything else it can get its lips on.

Oral-aggressive stage
After a short time, the infant begins to grow teeth. Then it learns to bite and it is a novel experience. It bites everything it can get its teeth onto.

Anal-expulsive stage
Newborn infants are not aware of their urinations and defecations.

When, eventually, they become aware they find the experience interesting and a source of pleasure.

Anal-retentive stage
When they begin to be potty-trained they become aware that they can control these functions and hold urine and faeces back. This is a new source of novelty and attracts praise from their parent for dry nappies.

Phallic stage
Between the ages of three and six children become aware of their own genitals as a source of amusement and pleasure. This becomes their new, primary source of stimulation.

Up to here, the children's devotion has centred on their opposite sex parent. In this stage jealousy over their same sex parent's relationship with the opposite sex parent rises to a peak in children of both sexes. At the end of this stage both sexes undergo an important transformation in their psychosexual development.

In males it results in what is known as the **Oedipus complex**, a taboo against erotic love of the mother. They become aware that female children have no protruding genitals and they assume they have been castrated by the father. They fear the same will happen to them for their attempts to win their mother's love instead of it going to their father. The fear causes their psyche to undergo a transformation. They *identify* with the father. In psychological terms this means they try to be identical to him in every way. The unconscious motive is that he would not want to hurt himself, so if they can make themselves match, as closely as possible, his identity they will be less likely to be mutilated by him. From then on their attraction to their mother is diminished and they enter the asexual, consolidation phase. There remains, however, the powerful taboo, stored in their memory against seeing their mother in an erotic way.

Freud argued that females undergo a similar transformation. Jung called it the **Electra complex**. Whereas males experience the fear that they will be castrated if their devotion to the opposite sex parent continues females come to the conclusion that they already have been. Thus, the complex leaves them with a tendency for guilt rather than inhibition, for while threat leads to inhibition punishment leads to guilt.

Guilt is a weaker restraining force on behaviour than inhibition and this led Freud to conclude that females have weaker consciences than men.

Consolidation stage

In this stage attention moves to rational pursuits – study, purposeful play, collecting, model building and so on. This is the only non-erotic stage of development.

Genital stage

In adolescence, the individual becomes aware of powerful urges and attention is focused, again, on genitalia – their own and those of partners and prospective partners. This new urge now becomes the dominant source of pleasure and a major source of motivation.

Transition through the stages

Parents allow children to behave in ways characteristic of particular developmental stages, sucking thumbs in early infancy, playing with the potty and being pre-occupied with deliberate urination and defecation when they get a little bit older, and so on. They don't let it go on forever, though. When the child has spent an appropriate time in each stage behaviour characteristic of it is discouraged. Thumb sucking is not encouraged after two years of age, nor playing with the potty, or being over attentive to urination or faeces, after about four years of age. The association between admonishment and the behaviours are stored in the memory, causing guilt or inhibition when, in the future, such behaviours are performed or contemplated.

At the same time as parents are ushering their children out of each behaviour phase the children themselves are becoming ready to drop the behavioural forms from their preferred repertoire. Where at first new behaviours are a novelty, eventually they become mundane and unexciting. This is due to the process of habituation, a non-associative type of memory storage, wherein each new occurrence of a stimulus is less exciting than the last, until it becomes completely mundane.

Abnormal development and its consequences

When things go wrong

If parents coerce children to give up a behaviour pattern too early, before they themselves have habituated to the stimulus of that stage, they will not be fully committed to moving on. The same can happen if parents have made a particular stage too comfortable for the child. They may not want to fully leave it. Part of them will stay in that stage and they will indulge in pseudo versions of the stage behaviours. In these maladaptive practices, the primary source of pleasure is recalled in recoded form and responded to in a similar fashion to before.

It is quite common to find individuals have some degree of fixation. For example, pipe smoking is the result of fixation in the oral incorporative stage. Nail biting is an indication of a fixation in the oral aggressive stage. Extreme messiness, or untidiness, is an indication of a fixation in the anal expulsive stage. Extreme tidiness is a manifestation of a fixation in the anal retentive stage. Where it is extreme, however, it causes problems in adult life.

Regression

If, in any stage, an individual experiences psychic conflicts, or levels of fear or anxiety that they cannot handle, their ego may regress them to an earlier phase where such conflicts or levels of anxiety did not occur, for the record of those earlier conditions still remains in memory.

Reaction formations

Sometimes the picture becomes a bit more complicated. A fixation in a developmental stage will make an individual recall and relive an immature desire in recoded form, such as the desire to live and work in a dirty environment that an anal expulsive individual will have. However, a reaction to this may be formed and stored in memory, because the fixation itself causes discomfort to the individual. Such reaction tends to produce behaviour opposite in form to that of the fixation, so that for example a tidiness or cleanliness obsession can result from an anal expulsive fixation. Any fixation can cause reaction formations.

The psychoanalytical explanation of mental behaviour is that it is motivated by a need to defend the ego, i.e. to avoid any threat to the reasonably comfortable balance being maintained by the competing forces of the id and the superego, or between impulse and restraint. Any threat will result in neurotic anxiety (a fear that the impulse will overwhelm restraint) or moral anxiety (a fear that restraint will be too strong to allow reasonable impulse satisfaction). Tactics for preventing threats to the ego are used throughout life.

Suppression
The most common tactic is suppression. When something makes us anxious we tend to suppress it (we often say we put it to the back of our mind – which is the same thing). When we suppress thoughts we put them into memory which is recallable by the conscious mind, but we then put other thoughts in the way – deliberate interference – to block recall.

Displacement – a type of unconscious recoding
If the anxiety an issue causes us is strong we may actually displace its object. That means unconsciously recoding the recall, so that the anxiety appears to be attached to something entirely different. A person who has just heard news of the death of their partner may become primarily preoccupied with anxiety over whether their cat is safe. An individual fearing redundancy may focus their anxiety on whether a pain, or harmless blemish on the skin is something more serious. The recoded fears are more manageable than the original ones. Possible danger to a pet is easier to handle than the death of a loved one and the possibility, but unlikelihood, that a blemish is malignant is easier to deal with than probable redundancy and financial ruin.

Where the anxiety comes from forbidden or shameful feelings or wishes, it is often dealt with by recoding their recall from memory in a different way. Shame and guilt, for example, may be dealt with by recoding the recall so that the bad, or blameworthy quality, or behaviour is attributed to another person. This individual is referred to as a scapegoat and the process is known as projection. Fears, guilt and shameful qualities can also be projected onto non-human animals, or objects. This is the way psychoanalysts explain phobias. In arachnophobia the spider carries the negative qualities, including the ability to evoke fear that primarily belonged to something else. The association has been unconsciously recoded on recall to make it more manageable. This may account for some cases of arachnophobia, although it must be said that there is strong evidence that most phobias are caused by simple stimulus and response conditioning (see Chapter 2). All any theory can do is explain some incidences, never all of them, otherwise it would be a *law*, not a theory.

If memory is the cause of neurotic symptoms then perhaps it is where we should look for the cure.

Repression

If the threat to the ego is extreme then rather than store it in the conscious mind, where we have access to it, we may store it in the unconscious, where we don't. This process, known as repression, is involuntary. Such threat might come from:

▶ powerful, degrading or frightening experiences
▶ forbidden or shameful wishes or feelings.

Not only is the storage involuntary, but so is recall. The repression process allows forbidden material to come through to the consciousness in recoded form. They are what we know as symptoms of psychological or physiological illness (in the latter case psychological in cause and physical in outcome).

Releasing repressed memories

If repressed memories cause problems can they be released? It would appear so, but not in the usual way you recall memories. The first problem is to find what the repressed memories are that are causing the problems. Psychoanalysts believe there are windows to the unconscious; they include dream content, slips of the tongue and free association (allowing your mind to produce audible rambling, saying whatever comes in to your head). In dreams, forbidden feelings and wishes are expressed in coded form and these codes can be transcribed. A regularity of symbol usage by, and associated symptoms of, dreamers has enabled psychoanalysts to build up a picture of what forbidden thoughts and wishes various symbols are likely to represent. Slips of the tongue tend to appear as complete chance occurrences, but psycho-analysts argue that nothing occurs by pure chance; there is a line of causality, which is normally held in check by repression. A slip of the tongue represents a failure of the repression mechanism.

Secondary repression
Repression of threatening feelings or experiences is known as primary repression. Where such repression has taken place, however, the same treatment is given to associated feelings and experiences; we bury them in the unconscious memory too for there is the risk that the chain of association made may lead to the recovery of the repressed material. This is known as *secondary repression* and makes the psychoanalyst's task of revealing repressed memories more difficult. Firstly, they act as a buffer to the repressed memories. Secondly, they may be mistaken for the primary repressions themselves.

Free association is a technique that is not so much a window on the unconscious as a diviner of buried memories. In psycho-analysis, the therapist encourages the client to allow their mind to generate what seem to be random ideas, saying everything that enters their head, without any attempt to order, or select from it. Whenever the flow comes to a sudden halt the therapist interprets this as evidence that there is a buried memory closely associated with the last word, or words uttered. The therapist then counsels the client with this area in focus, to try to discover what that buried memory might be.

Here, a second obstacle occurs – the buried memories are resistant to recovery. This often leads psychotherapists to make suggestions to the client as to what kind of memory it is which is resisting retrieval. It is here that a major threat to validity, or source of inaccuracy creeps in.

It may be possible to enhance the recall process by means of hypnosis.

If these buried memories can be brought to the surface their power to generate neurotic symptoms is neutralised. This is a process known as **abreaction**.

Neurotic symptoms often persist beyond abreaction, however, but where this is the case they can be explained in other ways. For example, where a repressed memory that caused a phobia is abreacted the phobia may continue as a result of the conditioning by the repeated associations between fear and the phobia object. Conditioning was dealt with in Chapter 2.

Tutorial

Seminar Discussion

1. What are the merits and demerits of the psychoanalytical approach? To what extent can it provide understanding of human memory?

2. Is repression an adequate explanation of physical symptoms, like eczema, psoriasis, asthma, etc?

3. Neurotic symptoms can persist after abreaction. Could this mean that repression is not involved?

Student assignment

Choose three characters in a soap opera (e.g. *Eastenders* or *Coronation Street*). Consider the way their parent(s) (and perhaps other authority figures) respond to them. Describe the effect such treatment might have on their personality development and the kinds of adult personality that can occur from such behaviour.

Practice Questions

1. Which one of the following is correct? In psychoanalytical terms, a fixation is:

   a. an obsession about something
   b. a regression to an earlier developmental stage
   c. correction of a phobia
   d. a developmental glitch.

2. Which two of the following are correct?

   a. Guilt is a stronger moral force than inhibition.
   b. Inhibition is a stronger moral force than guilt.

    c. Inhibition and guilt are equally strong moral forces.
    d. Guilt combined with inhibition is a stronger moral force than guilt alone.
    e. Neither is effective alone.

3. Which one of the following is correct? Strong anxiety can cause a person to:

    a. advance one stage
    b. regress one stage
    c. regress to any stage
    d. advance to any stage
    e. get stuck in the present stage.

4. Which of the following are correct? Undesirable memories are dealt with by:

    a. repression
    b. displacement
    c. suppression
    d. scapegoating
    e. any of these.

5. Choose the most appropriate pair of options.
Repressed memories:

    a. stay buried altogether
    b. are recalled into consciousness
    c. are not recalled into consciousness
    d. are re-coded on recall
    e. are coded on storage.

Bibliographical Notes

1. Harris (1970)

4

The Humanist Perspective on Memory

One-minute summary: A humanist perspective would focus on the content of memory. Individuals have free will as to what they learn and act on the basis of self-interest. Individuals seek enhanced self-esteem and this involves stores of normative data and actual data. Self-esteem level is the difference between our ideal and actual self-concepts. Autobiographical memory and reflex memory are sources of insecurity. Individuals seek power and security and their various knowledge stores, conscious and unconscious, can be a means to this.

This chapter will help you to understand:

▶ the human memory from a humanist perspective
▶ the aspects of human memory which would be of interest to psychologists working in the humanist tradition.

Humanist perspective

While most approaches to memory focus on the processes and hardware of human memory, a humanist perspective, more or less alone, would focus on what is actually stored.

This school of thought assumes people have choice about what they learn and what they store in their memories and that they make their choices on the basis of self-interest. Of course, these choices are, themselves, limited by predispositions that have a genetic basis. They are also conditioned by factors largely outside their control – past experience and treatment by others, which has led to various fears and insecurities. Human free will never amounts to *liberum arbitrium indifferentiae*.*[1] These differing pasts

---

[1]Freedom to the extent that nothing compels us to do or refrain from doing anything, not even our own nature.

which people have will lead them to differ in the knowledge and skill they are motivated to acquire and store in the various faculties of their brains.

The humanist perspective involves assumptions that individuals seek power, happiness, security, self-esteem and freedom. It assumes they have a desire to increase their knowledge and to actualise their potential. If we look at memory from this of point of view, we focus upon:

▶ the emotional and factual data of autobiographical memory
▶ the constraints instilled in our superego by our parents and other authority figures
▶ the skills in our procedural memory
▶ the knowledge and experience in our declarative memory.

Autobiographical memory and insecurity

Autobiographical memory and sources of insecurity

People's upbringing differs from person to person and their lives develop in different ways thereafter. Each autobiography has sources of insecurity, some more than others. If a person was isolated a lot as a child they will crave company for fear of re-living the feeling of isolation again. If their parents' marriage was unstable they will have lived in fear of losing one of their parents and, with it, their source of safety. If, as a child, they were small for their age they may have feared bullies. They may have had a facial disfigurement, a speech impediment, a limp, or they may have been over-weight. Any of these deviations from the norm would have been a reason for other children to pick on them. As they developed into adulthood, even though people ceased to persecute them, the fear would always be there, even if they were not always consciously aware of it.

Stored up insecurity influences adult behaviour and it is this sort of thing which has underlaid the rise to power of some of the biggest tyrants in history. It is known that both Napoleon and Hitler had significant sources of autobiographical insecurity. It sometimes seems to spur people on to great heights of power. Adler was the first psychologist to study the power motive in human beings.[2] He believed it is of paramount importance, as insecurity is our main motivating force. Acquiring power is a way of reducing this insecurity.

Declarative memory and power

It is often said that knowledge is power. It is certainly a major source or tool for wielding it. Many of the everyday power struggles that occur are in the competitive conditions of the market for jobs and the market for goods and services. The amount of appropriate knowledge and skill a person has clearly affects their power to compete successfully. This is a reason why many strive for a good education; it will give them more power in the marketplace.

Knowledge and political power

The more relevant knowledge a person has the more they can use it to control the behaviour of others. They can call upon the knowledge they have where it will help their cause and withhold it where it will not. Indeed, all the leaders in the world use these tactics, to some degree, to control the people over whom they govern. Stored social skills enhance people's power too, for example skills of negotiation, pacing and assertiveness. A person's self-esteem level is based upon the difference between what they assess themselves to be and what they feel they ought to be. This implies that two separate profiles are stored and compared – the *ideal self-concept* and the *actual self-concept*. These profiles of information begin and, for the most important part, are completed in the early years of life. Whether you are happy with yourself or feel you ought to do better is, to a large extent, down to the things your parents said to you in your early childhood.

Maslow believed that once the more basic needs, such as food, drink, shelter, warmth, safety and affiliation have been met people start to seek to enhance their self-esteem. This means bringing their actual self-concept more into line with their ideal self-concept.

Tutorial

Seminar discussion

Is the humanist perspective of any real value in the study of human memory?

Student assignment

Find two people who have been centrally involved in a common crisis, i.e. an accident, a heated dispute, or some other situation which tested their courage, strength, intelligence, resourcefulness and other aspects of their characters. Ask them both, separately, to describe what took place and the way those concerned responded to the situation, including the other person you are interviewing.

Compare their accounts. How much can a humanist approach inform your understanding of any discrepancies?

Practice questions

1. Which one of the following is most consistent with the humanist perspective? Individuals are motivated by:

   a. self-interest
   b. care for the human race
   c. self-denial
   d. care for fellow human beings
   e. realistic goals.

2. Which three of the following are the most consistent with the humanist approach to memory?

   a. individual behaviour is driven by self-interest
   b. individual behaviour is driven by altruism
   c. individual behaviour is driven by desire for power
   d. individual behaviour is driven by desire to reduce insecurity
   e. individual behaviour is driven by a sense of duty.

3. Which of the following is correct and which is false?

   a. humanists believe people have free will
   b. humanists believe that free will is a myth.

4. Which two are most consistent with the humanist approach? People seek power:

   a. because they desire it
   b. because of a sense of duty
   c. to use it to protect others
   d. to reduce their own insecurity
   e. to prevent others getting it.

5. Maslow believed people are:

   a. always motivated by the desire to enhance their self esteem
   b. sometimes motivated by desire to enhance their self-esteem
   c. never motivated by the desire to enhance their self-esteem
   d. always motivated by basic, biological and security needs
   e. motivated by desire to enhance their self-esteem only when more basic needs have been met.

Bibliographical notes

1   Schopenhauer (1974)
2   Adler (1917)

5

The Psychobiology of Memory

One-minute summary: Declarative and reflex memory have separate circuits. Reflex memory seems to be processed mainly in the cerebellum. Declarative memory seems to be processed mainly in the cerebrum. The hippocampus plays a very important part in storage. Different aspects of memory are stored at different sites. Memory has stages. Long-term, plastic changes are different from short-term plastic changes. Short-term memory involves dynamic changes and short-term plastic changes. Long-term memory involves growth of new protein. Habituation is a non-associative kind of memory process. Sensitisation is where an individual learns to react strongly to a stimulus. Inhibition is the opposite. Various kinds of electro-chemical processes underlie memory storage.

- ▶ the psychobiological approach to human memory
- ▶ the separate circuitry of declarative and reflex memory
- ▶ the stages of storage
- ▶ the various types of memory process
- ▶ where in the brain different memory processes take place
- ▶ the special role of a structure called the hippocampus
- ▶ the biological differences between short-term and long-term memory
- ▶ the neural processes underlying memory storage.

The psychobiological approach
Psychobiologists concern themselves with the neural substrate of memory processes. This means they are interested in the brain hardware and the electro-chemical processes which take place whenever we commit something to memory.

The separate circuits of declarative and reflexive memory

The reflex memory is the part of the brain where we store learned skills and procedures which have become automatic – riding a bike, for example. The recall and therefore the performance of such skills is a reflex action rather than a voluntary procedure, and this is why it is called the **reflex memory**.

The **declarative memory** is so called because its contents can be declared in sentences. Material is stored by means of associations made at the time of evaluating, comparing and drawing inferences from informational input.

There appear to be quite separate circuits for reflex memory and declarative memory processes in the human brain. Localised brain damage tends to affect one or the other, but not both.

Reflex memory circuitry

Reflex memory seems to be mainly processed in the cerebellum. Damage to the *medial** *dentate* and *lateral*† *interpositus* structures of the cerebellum, for example, have been found to eliminate a conditioned eye blink response.[1] This finding has been challenged by Bloedel *et al.*[2], who reported that the eye blink can be conditioned even after the cerebellum has been removed. It may be that parallel processes in the cerebellum can take over, or compensate.

Declarative memory circuitry

The cerebrum appears to be the domain of the declarative memory. While conducting temporal lobe surgery, Penfield[3] found that stimulating parts of the temporal lobe in conscious patients made them appear to recall autobiographical experiences (The validity of this study has, however, been challenged.) Conversely, Bickford *et al.*[4] found that electrical stimulation of part of the temporal lobe (the *mid temporal gyrus*, see Figure 1) produced brief retrograde amnesia.

Milner[5] found that patients who had had their hippocampus removed, to relieve symptoms of epilepsy, were unable to recall

---

* medial means towards the middle
† lateral means towards the side.

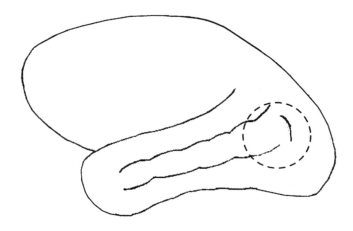

Figure 1. Region of the mid-temporal gyrus.

very recent memories and were unable to consolidate new ones to long-term memory.

Dual circuit involvement

Additional evidence of separate circuits is provided in performances that call upon, or can utilise both circuits. When tasks require both reflexive and declarative memory processes brain damaged, or amnesiac individuals can manage some parts of the task, but not others, depending on whether it is the temporal lobe or cerebellum which has been damaged.

People suffering from what is known as **Korsakoff's syndrome** suffer damage to their temporal lobe. In particular, the **mammillary bodies** and **medial dorsal nucleus** of the **thalamus** are affected. Korsakoff's syndrome is a brain deterioration, which results from chronic and severe alcoholism. As a result, sufferers lose their long-term memory ability, but can recall material after an interval if **priming** is used. Priming is a reflexive kind of memory. This effect demonstrates that while declarative memory is damaged reflexive memory need not be. This is also revealed in the case of other amnesiacs.

Stages of storage

Memory appears to have stages. Some are specific to particular types of memory. Here are some examples:

Iconic memory	half a second
Sensory memory	two seconds
Short-term memory	fifteen to thirty seconds
Extreme vulnerability phase	one hour
Span of potential retrograde amnesia (period during which long-term memory is still subject to potential disruption)	usually one to two years
Foreign language knowledge and skill	rate of forgetting levels out after about two years
Recognition of names and faces	good for thirty years and then declines steeply between thirty-five and fifty years
Memory for smells	more or less accurate up to thirty seconds and subject to 67–77% accuracy after thirty days.

Table 2. Types of memory storage and their durations.

Iconic memory
The iconic memory is the most transient of the memory processes. It concerns the retention of visual images and amounts simply to an after-image on the retina. The mechanism underlying it is a photochemical process.

Sensory memory
Sensory memory amounts to a reverberating echo in the inner ear and lasts approximately two seconds. It can be prolonged by rehearsal, because by repeating something to yourself, even in your head, you are continuously restarting the clock.

Short-term (or working) memory
Short-term memory lasts for between fifteen and thirty seconds.[6]

Consolidation period
After material has passed from short-term memory to long-term memory it is highly vulnerable to displacement for a period of about an hour and needs to be reinforced during that period.

Span of potential retrograde amnesia
Even material which has survived the consolidation period is vulnerable to disruption through brain trauma of one kind or another, for a period of between one and two years. Different memory processes seem to be subject to different stages.

Retention of foreign languages
Retention of foreign languages declines for about two years, then levels out.[7]

Name/face recognition
Recognition of names and faces seems to be good for thirty years on the average and then declines relatively steeply. Note, we are talking about recognition, not free recall. The latter is not so durable.

Procedural memory
Procedural memory is more durable than declarative memory.[7]

Olfactory memory
Memory for smells is particularly good, showing virtually no deterioration over a thirty second period and only about 30% deterioration (or 67%–77% accuracy of recall) over 30 days.[7]

Trace decay

Long-term memory is, in general, subject to gradual trace decay throughout life, quite apart from these stage-related decays. The life-long pattern follows rather a logarithmical curve.[7]

Changes underlying memory processes

Short-term memory can be partly explained as dynamic changes, i.e. reverberating loops of neurons, which are reciprocally exciting each other. 'A' excites 'B', 'B' excites 'C' and 'C' excites 'A'. There also appear to be some short-term plastic changes in the neural synapses. These changes are known as:

▶ presynaptic facilitation
▶ postetanic potentiation
▶ presynaptic inhibition
▶ postsynaptic inhibition
▶ habituation.

Presynaptic facilitation

Presynaptic facilitation occurs as a result of the action of a facilitating neuron releasing a neurotransmitter which reduces the K^+ (potassium ions) current and allows a build up of Ca^{2+} (calcium ions) in another neuron which, in turn, enhances its firing capacity.

Postetanic potentiation

Postetanic potentiation occurs as a result of a saturation of Ca^{2+} in a neuron.

Presynaptic inhibition

Presynaptic inhibition is where the action of one neuron depresses the Ca^{2+} current in another neuron, thereby reducing the amount of transmitter released.

Postsynaptic inhibition

Postsynaptic inhibition occurs when an inhibiting neuron hyperpolarises the cell body of another neuron, thus making the depolarisation required for firing less likely. Hyperpolarisation of a neuron is an increase in the difference of electrical charge on either side of the cell membrane. (See Figure 2.)

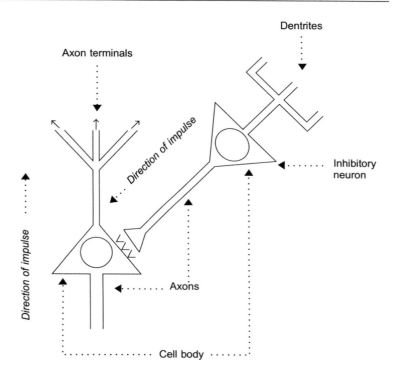

Figure 2. Model of a postsynaptic cell body receiving an impulse from an inhibitory neuron. This hyperpolarises it to make it less likely to fire.

Habituation

Habituation is a process whereby the build up of unimportant data leads the nervous system to begin to ignore a stimulus. It is believed that the short-term plastic change involved is, at least partly, the depression of the Ca^{2+} channel. This, in turn, reduces the inflow of Ca^{2+} ions, which control firing of the neuron.

Sensitisation

Sensitisation is a process whereby a person learns to react strongly to a particular stimulus, for example, a wasp flying close. Short-term sensitisation involves the build up of *cAMP (Cyclical Adenosine-Monophosphate)*, which leads, by a number of processes, to an increase in Ca^{2+} molecules in the cell. This, in turn, enhances the transmitter release.

Habituation and sensitisation can, to some degree, be reversed.

Long-term plastic changes

Long-term plastic changes are different from changes that underlie short-term memory. Long-term storage involves the activation of genes, the proteins of which have four important consequences:

▶ persistent activation of *cAMP*-dependent **protein kinase**
▶ growth of new synaptic terminals
▶ increase in proportion of active zones in synapses
▶ **dentridic** growth.

The persistent activation of *cAMP* (which, through *protein kinase*, leads to increased enhancement of transmitter release), the increase in the proportion of synaptic terminals and the proportion of active zones and the growth of new dendrites all serve to strengthen the synapses involved.

Long-term habituation is the reverse of the process. Here, synaptic terminals, proportion of active zones and dentridic growth all decrease.

Where in the brain do memory processes take place?

Memory processes take place in different areas of the brain, depending on which part of the process and what kind of memory is involved. The initial iconic memory for something seen is limited to the retina, though it is perceived in the visual cortex (see Figure 3). The retina contains M cells and P cells. The P cells deal with colour and the M cells deal with the rest.

If it survives the half-second long transient chemical process which produces the after-image, it will be encoded accoustically so the material will move to processing in the inner ear, even though it is primarily visual material. At this stage you will be subvocalising the features of the image, e.g. 'a house with four windows'. It is held here while the neural system searches for a match in long-term memory.

If a match is found the image will move to short-term memory. Here, it will last for between fifteen and thirty seconds. If it is attended to and meaningfully worked upon, it will be stored, by the action of the hippocampus, in various sites of the cerebrum.

So important is the role of the hippocampus and surrounding areas that damage generally impairs or even prevents altogether long-term storage. Assuming there is no such damage, the material passing into long-term memory will be stored in various sites, each dealing with a different aspect of perception – the movement aspect to the movement centres, the sound aspect to the sound centres and so on. There are centres for different aspects of perception. They include centres for:

► vision shape	► vision direction	► smell
► vision size	► vision colour	► taste
► vision texture	► vision movement	► touch
► vision depth	► sound	
► vision location	► speech	

Long-term storage of visual images
The primary visual cortex is in the occipital lobe, at the back of the brain. In it different sites deal with different kinds of image feature. There are sites, for example, dealing with size, texture and shape. The principle sub-cortical region for processing visual information is the *lateral geniculate nucleus*. (See Figure 3.)

Each visual cue is dealt with by several pathways in parallel and interactive processing and there are inputs from the attention processing areas in the pre-frontal cortex. It has been suggested that attention could act as a binding agent.[8]

The area principally involved in perception of shape and colour is known as the *parvo-cellular – interblob system* and the main area which deals with recognition of form, depth, figure ground, relative size and many visual illusions is known as the *magno-cellular system*. The perception of location and spatial organisation is dealt with in the posterior parietal cortex.

Motion is dealt with in the middle temporal areas V1,V2,V3 and V5 and the medial superior temporal area V5a. Neurons in the V1 area are selectively involved; they fire when motion is perpendicular to their angle of orientation. Area V4 deals with orientation and colour.

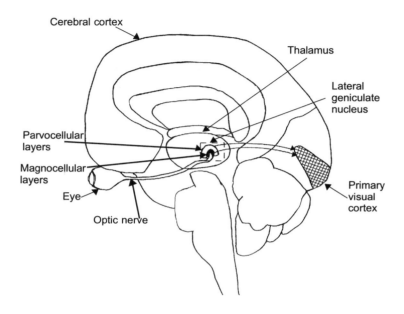

Figure 3. Regions of the brain where vision is processed.

The long-term storage of sound

The auditory cortex contains many areas to deal with such diverse inputs as amplitude, pitch, tempo and direction of sound. This cortex is in the temporal lobe close to the Fissure of Sylvius.

Storage of other sensory data

Taste is dealt with in the sensory cortex and smell is dealt with in the olfactory cortex. The latter has five parts:

▶ anterior olfactory nucleus
▶ anterior tubercle
▶ pyriform cortex
▶ amygdaloid complex
▶ entorhinal area (which projects into the hippocampus).

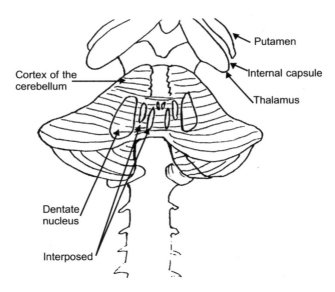

Figure 4. Dentate nucleus and Interposed.

The thalamus also appears to be involved. The perception of touch is processed in an area known as the somatosensory cortex.

Reflex memory
As has already been pointed out, reflex memory appears to be mainly processed in the cerebellum but different sites, not all of them cerebellar, appear to process different kinds of reflexes, for example:

► amygdala – conditioned heart rate
► medial dentate nucleus and lateral interpositus – conditioned eye-blink response. (See Figure 4.)

The neural processes involved in memory

Short-term sensitisation
Different processes underlie different kinds of memory effects. Let's deal first with the simplest ones.

The physiological process in iconic memory is a transient change in the retina, lasting half a second or less. The physiological substrate of sensory memory is a reverberating loop of sound in the inner ear.

Postetanic potentiation

Postetanic potentiation is a situation where tetanic stimulation of a neuron leads to a saturation of Ca^{2+}. This, in turn, acts to increase the quantity of transmitter release vesicles arriving at the release sites. This simple, cellular level memory process can last between several minutes and an hour.

Presynaptic facilitation

Have you noticed how the presence of a mildly distracting sound will become more distracting as time goes on? Pulling a sticking plaster off a hairy part of the skin will become more painful at each pull and a bad smell will get worse to the nose until you have to remove yourself from its vicinity. This is because a kind of cellular memory process is at work wherein seratonin and other neurotransmitters flow, by way of axo-axonal, synaptic connections between interneurons and sensory neurons. The seratonin (5HT) activates a series of serial and parallel, intracellular processes which enhance transmitter release and, thus, prolong the action potential. It is known as presynaptic facilitation.

The seratonin acts through a second messenger *cyclical AMP* (known as *cAMP*) to reverse the electrical charge of the cell so that the K^+ gate is closed. This prolongs the influx of Ca^{2+}, which is what triggers transmitter release. This reversal of the electrical charge is known as phosphorylation (introduction of a phosphoryl group to the substrate, or cell body).

Sensitisation and the effects of practice
Practice enhances storage in a graded way.

Example:

one trial	sensitisation for four minutes
four trials	sensitisation for one day
more trials	sensitisation for one week

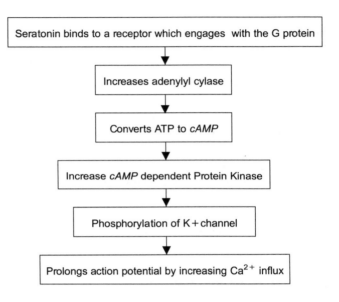

Figure 5. The neurochemistry of sensitisation.

The process is summarised in Figure 5.

Presynaptic inhibition
At axo-axonal synapses a messenger can be sent from a presynaptic inhibitory neuron to another presynaptic neuron, which has the effect of depressing Ca^{2+} influx. This will reduce the amount of neurotransmitter released from it.

Postsynaptic inhibition
Inhibition can also be achieved by an inhibitory neuron synapsing on the cell body of a second neuron, rather than on its axon, or dentrites. This increases the difference in electrical charge on either side of the cell membrane – a process known as **hyperpolarisation.** When a cell is hyperpolarised, the likelihood that it will fire decreases. This kind of inhibitory process is called **postsynaptic inhibition.**

Habituation

Habituation is a kind of cellular memory process, which reduces the effect of sensitisation to a stimulus. If we see something we have not seen before, smell something we have not smelt before, or hear something new our sensitivity to it will increase for a while. This is due to the build up of Ca^{2+} in the cell membrane, increasing the amount of transmitter released. After a while, though, the N type Ca^{2+} channel in the pre-synaptic neuron will be deactivated, restricting the inflow of Ca^{2+} and this, in turn, will lead to a decrease of this in the cell. Since it is Ca^{2+} that determines transmitter release the latter will decrease too. The effect will be experienced as habituation to the stimulus, i.e. the stimulus simply loses its power to stimulate.

Habituation and facilitation can be short-term, or long-term. Both involve:

► strengthened synaptic connections
► enhanced transmitter release
► involvement of seratonin and *cAMP*.

Long-term facilitation effects derive from an increase in the number of synapses and growth of membrane areas. They therefore require activation of genes and new protein growth. The process is shown in Figure 6.

Long-term habituation is the reverse of this process. Dentrites, proportion of active zones and number of terminals actually decrease.

Classical conditioning

Classical conditioning is a reflex memory process. It is the mechanism through which we learn our habitual, or unconscious, automatic behaviours. It takes place when something that occurs immediately before, or in very close contiguity with, a reward becomes associated in the mind with that reward. The stimulus of both the non-rewarding event and the rewarding event will each cause their own individual neuronal firings and the association will be made. Thereafter, the former event will be experienced as rewarding in itself.

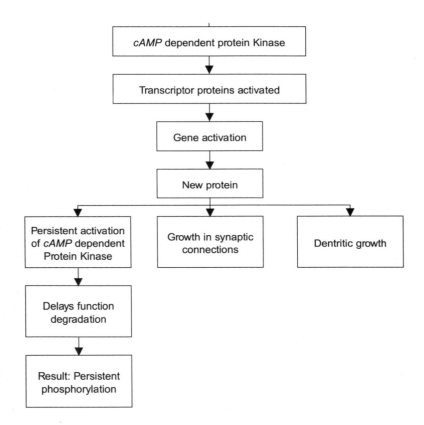

Figure 6. The neurochemistry of long-term facilitation.

What is going on at a physiological level to establish this response is that the neurons activated in the conditioned stimulus (non-rewarding event) pathway start the process of Ca^{2+} influx and this amplifies the process which takes place when the unconditioned stimulus (the rewarding event) is applied.

The *cAMP* must be just the right quantity – too much or too little undermines classical conditioning.

Long-term potentiation in the CA1 region of the hippocampus
Long-term potentiation (the neurochemical mechanism under-lying long-term memory) in the CA1 region of the hippocampus requires activation of many *afferent pathway* fibres together. It will

not occur by activation of a single fibre. Furthermore, both presynaptic and postsynaptic membranes must be activated and they must match.

Postsynaptic event
Several bursts of activity from fibres in the afferent pathways send the neurotransmitter glutamate to bind on two receptors of a postsynaptic membrane. These receptors are known as the NMDA receptor and the non-NMDA receptor. It is the non-NMDA receptor which makes the next move in the process. The NMDA receptor acts as a gateway, doubly blocked by both an electrical charge and a *chemical sentry*, you might say. The chemical is Mg^{2+}. When glutamate binds to its neighbouring non-NMDA receptor it causes it to phosphorylate the cell. This means it reverses the electrical charge of the cell and this unlocks the gateway of the NMDA receptor. At the same time it removes the Mg^{2+} blockade. Ca^{2+} can now flow into the cell. This chemical, once inside the cell, activates what are known as second messengers. There are two of them:

▶ Ca 2^+ calmodulin dependent kinase
▶ protein kinase C.

These, in turn, activate what is known as retrograde plasticity factor, which leaves the cell and crosses the synaptic cleft to the presynaptic membrane. There it penetrates the cell and activates a second messenger, which enhances transmitter release in that cell.

LTP in the CA3 region of the hippocampus is slightly different. It still requires an increase in transmitter release and the process is still activated by the neurotransmitter glutamate, in this case deriving from the mossy fibres of the granule cells of the dentate nucleus. Unlike LTP in the CA1 region, however, multiple excitation and matching of pre- and postsynaptic fibres is not necessary. The NMDA receptor gate plays no part in the process, nor does the molecule Ca^{2+}. It is not fully understood how the mechanism in this form of LTP works, but it is known that norepinephrine plays a part, working through what is known as the *cAMP* cascade.

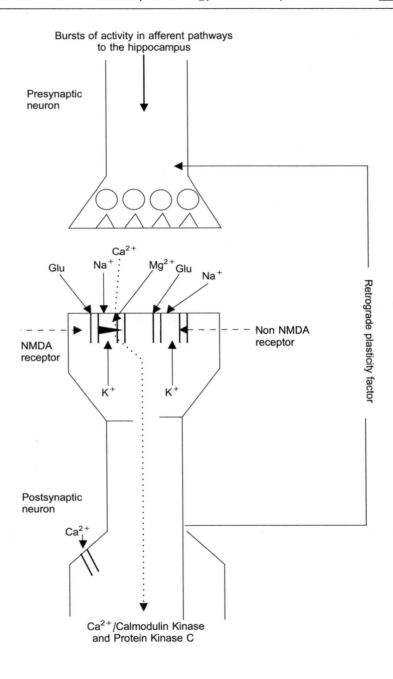

Figure 7. The process of long-term potentiation (LTP) in the hippocampus.

Tutorial

Seminar discussion
What are the strengths and weaknesses of a psychobiological approach to understanding human memory?

Student assignment
Try to explain, in psychobiological terms, why:

- ▶ We duck automatically if something is thrown at us.
- ▶ We cease to be alarmed about something once we know it will not harm us.
- ▶ We learn new knowledge on our college courses.
- ▶ We learn a new skill such as typing, playing an instrument, or swimming a new stroke
- ▶ Phobias can be treated by therapists.

Questions and answers
1. Which three of the following options are correct?

   a. declarative memory and reflex memory seem to share the same circuitry

   b. declarative memory and reflex memory seem to have different circuitry

   c. declarative memory and reflex memory circuitry seem to be mainly in the cerebellum

   d. reflex memory circuitry seems to be mainly in the cerebellum and declarative memory in the cerebrum

   e. circuitry of neither of these memory types is accurately known for certain.

2. Which three of the following options are correct? The hippocampus is:

   a. an image store

   b. an important component in the memory process

   c. part of the diencephalon

   d. nothing to do with memory

   e. involved in the transmission from short-term memory to long-term memory.

3. Which two of the following are correct?

    a. memory, once stored, remains stable
    b. memory, once stored, gradually fades
    c. memory, once stored, strengthens itself
    d. memory, once stored, goes through identifiable stages
    e. nobody knows what happens to it.

4. Which three of the following are correct?

    a. short-term memory is the same process as long-term memory
    b. short-term memory is a different process to long-term memory
    c. short-term memory involves dynamic changes and plastic changes
    d. long-term memory involves plastic changes and new protein growth
    e. short-term memory involves new protein growth

Bibliographical notes

1   Thomson (1988)
2   Bloedel et al (1991)
3   Penfield (1958)
4   Bickford et al (1958)
5   Milner (1971)
6   Kandell, Schwartz and Jessell (1991)
7   Baddeley (1996)
8   Treisman (1988)

Social Psychology of Memory

One-minute summary: What is stored and later recalled will be influenced by the expectations of others. The type of question asked influences material recalled. This has implications for validity of eye-witness testimony and the findings of RMT (recovered memory therapy) practitioners. The recall context may be different from the storage context and so the memory will be changed on re-storage. Things like the degree of independence of mind will mediate a social effect. Some social groups value memory quality highly and promote use of enhancement techniques. Some aspects of modern life have damaging effects on memory quality.

In this chapter, you will learn about:

▶ how other people's expectations affect what we recall
▶ how the type of question we are asked influences what we recall
▶ practical uses for memory techniques
▶ modern technology and memory quality
▶ the weaknesses of eye-witness testimony.

Social effects on autobiographical memory

Social effects on memory can be quite profound. Baddeley[1] tells of a situation where having heard about a particular event shared by a group of colleagues, he eventually recounted his experience of the event only to find his colleagues looking at him in amazement. Then one of them remarked that he had not been there. Suddenly he realised this was so. He had heard the tale so often that it had become spun into his autobiographical memory as if it were a personal experience. More will be said in explanation of this kind of memory phenomena in Chapter 7.

Social roles have expectations attached to them and these will affect recall in some situations. In the Asch experiments subjects were found to recall what was expected of them even though what they recalled was inaccurate.[2]

Group affiliation

Material is interpreted before it is stored and this interpretation will vary from person to person. Such interpretation is influenced by the outlook of the groups to which individuals affiliate.

When it is recalled it is reinterpreted, and the new interpretation will be influenced by the values, beliefs and orientations of the group to which an individual affiliates at the time of recall. This may be different from that which applied when the information was initially stored. An example is the way that elderly people frequently recall quality of life in bygone times as better than in the present day. The evidence from the history books tells us that the reality was quite different.

Susceptibility to social influence

Some people are more influenced by social effects than others. Stage hypnotists quickly pick out such people from the audience after a few simple tests and select them to take part in their performances. Everyone knows the expectations which are attached to the role of hypnotism subject and these individuals are more than usually compelled to comply. They are not being dishonest; it's just that expectations are a relatively important determinant of their behaviour. They are not even aware that this is the case. It need be no more dishonest to distort perceptions to fit in with the expectations of others than it is to distort them to make them consistent with your own perceptual system. We all do the latter and it is done unconsciously and innocently.

Degree of independence of mind

Two kinds of social influence can be distinguished:

► desire to be liked
► desire to be right.

When desire to be liked is very strong an individual may express their recollections in a way that is consistent with those of others, though they may not totally believe in what they are saying.

The desire to be right is also a major source of social influence. Individuals may feel that if all the other group members interpret an event in a particular way that is likely to be the way it actually was.

Group affiliation

Events are interpreted and understood differently by each group, for example, those in favour of a decision to use a particular rural site for a new road will see things very differently from a group of anti-road protesters at the site. They will select for attention different facts from those of the protesters and they will interpret them in ways which will make them consistent with their own conceptual scheme.

Not only is storage subject to deletion, distortion and generalisation, it is also affected by expectations and group pressure. The deletions, distortions and generalisations, and also the group expectations and pressures will differ significantly between the pro-road and anti-road groups. The anti-road group members are likely to register more violence on the part of the police than those in favour of the road project. They, themselves, are likely to be aware of more violence on the part of the protesters than the latter will note. If we start out with the belief that one party is in the wrong we are more likely to see those things which will support this view than those things which do not. When we recall the information we interpret it yet again, modifying it as necessary in order to make it consistent with our current general outlook. It is not lying; it is a matter of limitations of perceptual set, cognitive economics and an innate drive to make things consistent.

Social groups and memory values

Some social groups place high value on memory quality. The Masonic Society is an example. Some religious groups (e.g. Muslims, Judaism) do likewise, for they expect their clerics to know the scriptures so well that they can recall the very page, and position thereon, of particular pieces of text.

Some groups more than others indulge in practices which have damaging effects on memory – marijuana users for example. This drug has a damaging effect on short-term memory and long-term users often admit that their short-term memory has become very poor as a result of using the drug.

Nicotine and amphetamines actually aid consolidation – the process of storage into long-term memory. The negative effects on the body in other ways, however, greatly outweigh the positive effects and cigarette smoking can increase the likelihood of an individual suffering a stroke. This can have a highly damaging effect on memory. So don't be tempted by the consolidational benefits.

Groups where drug usage is the norm will invariably use LSD and other hallucinogenic drugs. This practice leads to long-term storage of invalid perceptions and these will have distorting effects on recall of other material. In addition, LSD users become prone to flashbacks, i.e. reliving of induced hallucinations. This is not surprising, as our mental storage system cannot file them separately as hallucinatory experiences, so that they are not relived in the normal way. Just as it is normal for us to relive previous real experiences, the hallucinatory ones will present themselves, on appropriate cues, for reliving too.

Excessive alcohol use has seriously deleterious effects on memory and in some sub-groups drinking to excess is the norm. Often such people are vagrants and long-term alcoholics. A long-term consequence of this condition is Korsakoff's syndrome, which damages the diencephalon. This leads to failure to consolidate and a tendency to confabulate.

The social mind set and the limits of social knowledge will affect what is perceived in the first place and, therefore, what will subsequently be stored in long-term memory and, perhaps, even be transmitted down the generations. Indeed, this has been the basis of some explanations of Biblical events and Greek mythology. Objects and processes not yet understood and not yet forming part of the human schemata may have been interpreted in a way that makes them consistent with human knowledge at the time – aircraft becoming flying horses, beings with rocket backpacks being perceived as angels and floods which stretch as far as can be seen being perceived as floods which encompass the whole world.

Societal type

The type of society, its structure, its outlook and the way it exploits its resources will influence the kinds of memory qualities which flourish. Evolutionary forces will favour whatever kind of memory process is most appropriate for adaptation to the conditions of life. Memory skills will flourish to the extent that they enhance the kind of memory ability most needed. If superior memory for numbers or text is unlikely to benefit a member of a primitive, hunting and gathering society as much as a superior reflex memory, or memory for geographical routes, individuals with the latter form of superiority will be more successful and, therefore, more likely to pass on their genes.

In an industrialising society skill development is at a premium and superiority in procedural memory will give individuals the edge. In Victorian Britain, tradesmen were respected as a class and had a reasonably high social status. They were proud to say they were good with their hands rather than their heads. Now things have changed. Physical skills are not valued so much because machine processes have replaced them. Today it is declarative memory which is highly regarded. Memory for knowledge is most important.

Non-literate societies

Where societies have little or no use of paper or printing, a greater amount has to be held in memory. In addition, knowledge tends to be encoded into easily memorisable forms. The ancient Greeks devised mnemonic methods, which are still used today. The itinerant teachers (the sophists) would memorise their lectures by walking through buildings and mentally attaching each important point to a different room. When they gave their lectures they would mentally walk through the buildings again and mentally collect each point as they entered each subsequent room.

The Romans used what tends to be known as the **room system**. It was first noted to have been used by Simonides, who after attending a banquet where the building collapsed, had astounded people by being able to recall the names of everyone who had attended. They would keep a particular room in their heads for the purpose. It would contain a few items of furniture – never cluttered. When they wished to remember things they would imagine them placed on each item of furniture. The main difference between the **Method of Loci** and the room system is that the room system uses the same room all the time, while the Greek Sophists used a different building for each lecture.

In non-literate societies social knowledge is encoded into epics (long stories), fables (shorter stories) and poems. Words of wisdom tended to be expressed in statements which had rhyme and rhythm. For example:

Red sky at night,
Shepherds' delight.

In these forms the wisdom can be easily remembered, re-told and passed down from generation to generation. The form in which it is held also restricts distortion to some degree, but does not protect it from change altogether.

The weakness of story forms in preventing distortion is evident when stories are re-told from person to person in a group. By the time the story gets to the last person it is very different from the form in which it started. The plot is the same, but the details get changed. This is because each person recalls it in a way that makes sense to them and is consistent with their own conceptual scheme.

There is an anti-mnemonics lobby. Some academics hold the view that the only thing you can use mnemonics for is trivia; you can't use them for anything useful. They point to the fact that even if you can learn factual information you will only be able to regurgitate it without understanding. Some teachers hold the view that using memory techniques amounts to cheating. It is true that memory techniques can never replace learning, but the memory training movement never claims they can. What they can do is enable people to hold larger structures of information in their heads while they consider them, or perform operations on them. This indisputably must aid learning. Memory techniques can also enable you to absorb into your mind a series of facts which you can recall later for consideration and manipulation at times when there is little else to do – when travelling, waiting for a bus, travelling on a bus, waiting in a dentist's surgery and so on.

Centuries ago René Descartes acknowledged that if we can improve our ability to **chunk** (enhance short-term memory) we can improve our intelligence.[3]

Practical uses for memory techniques

By training their memory, sales people and others employed in customer or industrial relations can improve their social effectiveness in that they can readily recall to mind names of customers or employees, together with little things that make them feel they are important. Language learners can speed up their progress and pupils of all subjects can pack more detail into their minds, in readily recollectable form, so that they can achieve 100 per cent recall in exams. There can be no reasonable doubt that memory training has beneficial effects for people in modern society.

Furthermore, there is a kind of intelligence which is based on memory. It is known as crystallized intelligence. It develops through schemata formation. Schemata is the plural of schema, a knowledge structure, the internal representation of external reality. The more we store in schemata the more complex they become, so that the more external experiences we can match with them without distortion. Therefore the more we store, the more we readily understand the world, because the more equal are our internal and external worlds. This is the kind of intelligence that is based on lessons of the past and it is, therefore, arguably the most useful. The counterpart 'fluid intelligence' (which seems in some degree to be based on speed of thinking) deteriorates throughout life, while crystallized (wisdom-based) intelligence goes on increasing.

Modern technology and memory quality

Modern technology has also produced a range of drugs which are claimed to aid memory, like *Choline*, *Hydergene* and *DHEA*, the latter of which is used to treat Alzheimer's disease in the USA. Older remedies such as Ginkgo Biloba extract have also been reported to have positive effects on memory quality.

Some of the fall-out from industrial processes is believed to be damaging to memory quality. Aluminium has been cited as a suspected factor in Alzheimer's disease, for example. More recently, the use of mobile phones has been linked to memory loss, as a result of the microwave radiation involved heating up the brain. The data is ambiguous however.

Modern life is fast moving and this causes a high level of stress and anxiety. Both can have negative effects on memory quality.

One of the benefits of the modern age is prolonged life, but this brings its own problems in terms of memory quality. Alzheimer's disease is associated with advancing years, although it does sometimes strike younger people. The greater the proportion of elderly people in society the greater the number of Alzheimer's sufferers there will be.

Socially aided recall and re-storage

Where memories are recovered or reconstructed with the help of other people, this will invariably lead to distortion of recall. It will also distort subsequent re-storage for future recall. We all distort what we experience to some degree, to make it fit our perceptual set and our framework of understanding. Since we are all unique in terms of our genetic make-up and the conditions of our development, no two people's perceptual sets and frameworks of understanding can be expected to be the same. If others help us to recover, or reconstruct memories of the past, then their perceptual sets and frameworks of understanding are going to affect the outcome.

This can have important consequences for both individuals and the societies in which they live. They fall under two headings:

▶ the recovered memory therapy (RMT) movement
▶ eye-witness testimony in court hearings.

There has been a recovered memory therapy movement for a long time. It refers to a version of psychotherapy wherein practitioners help people recover repressed memories. Common recollections reported include abduction by aliens, satanic ritual abuse and past lives. These are invariably induced by help and guidance of the practitioners. The perceptual sets and frameworks of understanding of the therapists concerned will, therefore, have a distorting affect on what is reconstructed. Indeed, therapists sometimes use free association techniques, asking clients to let their imagination flow freely and to articulate every thought that comes into their head. The therapist may then tell them the reason why particular thoughts came into their head was because they came from a past life, from a repressed abduction by aliens, or satanic or ritual abuse in childhood.

These therapists invariably believe (or, at least, have a vested interest in the possibility) that satanic, ritual abuse and/or alien abduction goes on, and/or that reincarnation is a fact. This will inevitably influence their interpretation of their clients' articulations in therapy. These interpretations will be fed back to their clients, altering the content of their memories and their beliefs about their past experiences.

The social consequences of this practice have been immense. In the past decade, whole communities have come under suspicion of institutionalised, satanic ritual abuse. In the North of England and the Orkney Islands during the early 1990s for example, the emergence of a few reports of evidence of satanic, ritual abuse of children, from recovered memories induced by therapists, fuelled a belief among social workers that the problem was rife. Newspapers orchestrated the issue until it became a nationwide moral panic. This, in turn, fed back into the investigation and fuelled the discovery of even more cases. Children were taken into care by the local authorities while investigations went on. The actions and attitudes of social services departments appeared to have moved into the realms of public hysteria, before the cases all collapsed for want of evidence, when a degree of sanity returned. The children were returned to their parents, but it is arguable that the damage to them, their families and their communities could never be completely undone.

The weaknesses of eye-witness testimony

The other category of concern in respect of recovered memories is eye-witness testimony in court cases. It is now well established[4] that the words used when counsel cross-questions a witness about an event will influence their recall. Courts now refer to questions that influence a witness's recall as leading questions and tend to allow objections to them. The influence of other people is only part of the explanation for these sources of memory distortion. They are partly due to an innate drive for cognitive consistency present in the psychological makeup of human beings. This is the subject of the next chapter.

Tutorial

Seminar discussion
1. Is memory quality becoming less important, or more important in modern society?
2. How much can we trust eye-witness testimony in courts?
3. Discuss the social implications of RMT.

Student assignment
Download the short video clip from the memory site (www.memorysite.co.uk). The instructions for downloading will be given on the web page. Select a sample of 15 people. Ask each of them to watch the clip and then ask them to assess the speed of the car. Use:

Question 1 for the first group of five.
Question 2 for the second group of five.
Question 3 for the third group of five.
Question 1: How fast was the car going when it collided with the second car?
Question 2: How fast was the car going when it bumped the second car?
Question 3: How fast was the car going when it smashed into the second car?

Compare the speed assessment of each group.

Practice questions

1. Which two are correct?

    a. What we recall is entirely our affair and no one else's.

    b. Other people have an input on people's recall.

    c. We consciously choose whether to let others influence our recall.

    d. What people store in their memories is influenced by other people.

    e. What people store in their memories is not influenced by other people.

2. Which of the following are correct?

    a. Desire to be liked influences compliance with social pressure.

    b. Desire to be right influences compliance with social pressure.

    c. Both desire to be liked and desire to be right influence compliance with social pressure.

    d. Neither desire to be liked or desire to be right influence compliance with social pressure.

3. Eye-witness testimony is the best evidence in court cases – true/false. *(delete as applicable.)*

4. Which four of the following most accurately describe RMT? RMT involves:

    a. releasing repressed memories

    b. past life regression

    c. recovered memories of satanic ritual abuse

    d. recovered memories of abduction by aliens

    e. helping people to cope with painful memories.

5. Which of the following is true and which is false:

    a. Modern life has a beneficial effect on human memory quality.

   b. Modern life has a damaging effect on human memory quality.

Bibliographical notes

1. Baddeley (1996b)
2. Asch (1956)
3. Descartes (1998)
4. Loftus and Palmer (1974)

7

Reconstructive Memory

One-minute summary: The validity of **reconstructive memory** is not as good as people think. This is due to a double (and often multiple) level of interpretation. When people are emotionally aroused, they may, innocently, confabulate untrue stories. The Gestalt school of psychology assumes we have a need to change details to make our memories consistent. Piaget saw autobiographical memory as dynamic and continuously adjusting to achieve equilibrium. Many things can affect the accuracy of the recall.

In this chapter you will learn about:

▶ reconstructive memory and its implications in the larger social context
▶ double interpretation
▶ confabulation
▶ the view of the Gestalt school
▶ schemata theory
▶ the kind of things that can influence what is recalled.

Reconstructive memory and its implications

In the 1930s Bartlett began to show that memory is an imaginative reconstruction, to make the data we have of past events logical and coherent in terms of our present understanding. This is demonstrated whenever stories are passed on from person to person (or from generation to generation). Hunter[1] found that by the time a story has been passed on six or seven times it:

▶ has shrunk by about half
▶ has become more conventional
▶ has become more coherent
▶ has become more clichéd.

Autobiographical memory is particularly prone to error. This has important implications. Firstly, eye-witness testimony in legal cases cannot be taken at face value.[2] In addition, some well-publicised child abuse cases in the last decade were both founded on and defeated by the quality of reconstructive memory.

Double interpretation

The main problem with reconstructive memory is that it is subject to a double level of interpretation. First, we interpret experiences at the time they occur, making deletions and distortions as necessary to make them comprehensible and consistent. Without deleting the majority of features our perception would overload. We attend to only about one per cent of all the data present. Later, when we seek to recall it, parts of the experience will have become inaccessible, due to various sources of forgetting (see pages 24–7). The gaps are filled in with whatever material is available. This may include bits of dreams (daydreams and night dreams), material from stories, rumours, and so on.

Furthermore, when we recall an event we are to some degree reliving it. Just as we made deletions and distortions when we first experienced the event, so we will make deletions and distortions again, this time to make it consistent with our current thinking. If several years have passed since the event, our schemata and current thinking patterns will have changed, so our interpretation will be different this time.

Confabulation

Even more serious is the process of confabulation. When individuals are in a state of extreme emotional arousal they tend to make up information which will make their account of events coherent, consistent and logical. This is not exactly culpable lying, for at the time they may not be very aware of the falsity of their statements. Sufferers of Korsakoff's syndrome, a brain deterioration condition resulting from extreme alcohol abuse, are particularly prone to this.

Loftus[2] found that when eye-witness testimonies of events are elicited the witnesses distort their recall to some degree to make it consistent with the state of affairs implied by the form of questions they receive. For example, if a witness is asked if they saw *the* smashed headlight at the scene of an accident they are more likely to say yes than if they are asked if they saw *a* smashed headlight. Loftus also tested the effect on recall of the verbs used in the questions. This is what she found:

Words used	Average speed reported
smashed	40.8
bumped	38
collided	39.9
contacted	31.8

Table 3. Verbs used to question witnesses to an accident related to the speed they reported a vehicle was travelling immediately before collision.

It is, of course, tempting to say that it may just have been their reports that the leading questions were influencing, rather than their actual recall of events. However, testing after a week produced similar results, suggesting that the whole schema was affected.

Can Hypnosis Help?
If the whole schemata is affected then it would follow that hypnosis cannot get at the undistorted truth, for it is no longer there. Loftus argued that neither hypnosis nor truth serums are helpful in extracting the truth. Moreover, she argued that hypnosis makes people more suggestible and susceptible to leading questions.

The Gestalt psychology of memory

So far we have been talking mainly about recall, but this drive for consistency also affects storage. The Gestalt school of psychology, founded by people like Wertheimer, Koffka, Kohlar and Lewin, argued that learning should not be seen simply as the storage of stimulus–response associations, nor that human knowledge is built up as the sum of the parts. Rather, they argued that human knowledge must be viewed as an organised, constructed whole (a Gestalten). New learning does not simply add to this, it must be coherently fitted into it. This will invariably mean some degree of modification of what is already there.

Schemata theory

Assimilation and accommodation

During the course of our lives we are continuously making changes to the representation of the world we hold in our memory and also to our perceptual set and perceptual processes by which we take in new experiences. The purpose is to develop an increasingly faithful and coherent representation of the external world in our heads. Everything we hear or see, we integrate into that internal representation (known as schemata) and to do this we have to both adjust the schemata and distort the experience in order to make it fit. Piaget called this assimilation and accommodation. Assimilation refers to distorting the experience. Accommodation refers to making adjustments in the schemata. The dynamic which causes this to occur is a drive for equilibration between the external world and the internal world. If we did not have this drive we would not learn. The more readily something will fit into our present schemata the more likely it is to be remembered.

Influences

The reorganisation involved calls upon mental faculties such as intuition and creativity. It is not only the factual knowledge which it must integrate with, it must be consistent with things like attitudes, values, orientations and self beliefs. Research has shown that well proven, factual knowledge will be rejected, despite its merits, if it challenges strongly held religious beliefs.

People with high self-esteem experiencing failure in any aspect of their lives reorganise their memory of the circumstances so that the blame does not appear to lie with them. Similarly, when they encounter success they tend to reorganise their memory of the circumstances so that other people's contributions are minimised and their own maximised. People with low self-esteem tend to do the reverse, that is reorganise their knowledge of the circumstances surrounding their successes so that their own contribution is minimised. Where failure is concerned they minimise the influence of others and maximise their own blame. In this way they maintain a coherent internal representation of the world.

Tutorial

Seminar discussion
How far back can you remember? How much of it is likely to be accurate?

Student assignment
Download the story 'The War of the Ghosts' from the memory site *www.thememorysite.co.uk*. Select a group of six volunteers. Read the story to one of the volunteers, making sure that none of the others can hear it. Do not give the written text to the volunteer. Instruct that volunteer to tell the story verbally to a second volunteer and to tell that person to narrate it to a third volunteer, and so on. Finally, ask all the volunteers to write down the story, without conferring with each other.

Assess how much the story has changed and the degree to which the changes conform to the changes that Hunter reported (see page 90).

Practice questions
1. Which three are correct?

   a. once a memory is stored it remains unchanged

   b. once a memory is stored it remains unchanged, even if a little faded

   c. once a memory is stored it can change

    d.   once a memory is recalled it is reinterpreted and restored

    e.   the re-storage will change the old record.

2. Autobiographical memory is:

    a.   a faithful record of the past

    b.   a record of how you would have liked things to have happened

    c.   a store of fiction

    d.   a mixture of what did happen and what did not

    e.   an imaginative reconstruction of events.

3. Which two are correct? Accommodation is:

    a.   distortion of perception

    b.   distortion of schemata

    c.   acceptance of perception

    d.   both distortion of perception and distortion of schemata

    e.   neither.

4. By the time a story has been passed on six or seven times it has:

    a.   shrunk by half and become more unconventional

    b.   become less coherent and more clichéd

    c.   become more conventional and more coherent

    d.   shrunk by one third and become more coherent and clichéd

    e.   shrunk by about half.

5. Which is not correct? Autobiographical memory contains:

    a.   photographic images of the past

    b.   storage of actual things which did happen

    c.   imaginative reconstructions of events

    d.   facts and fictions.

Bibliographical Notes

1   Hunter, I. (1964)
2   Loftus and Palmer (1974)

8

Memory Impairment

One-minute summary: Some neurotic illnesses have a profound but temporary effect on memory quality. Drug abuse affects it in various ways, depending on the type of drug. Cardiovascular disease can result in strokes and haemorrages to the brain and these cause memory impairment. With the exception of a certain key site in the hippocampus, it is quantity of damage rather than the site of damage to the brain which counts most in terms of memory impairment. Memory quality declines with age, some types of memory more than others.

In this chapter you will learn about effects on memory from:

▶ neurosis
▶ chemical abuse
▶ trauma
▶ physical illness
▶ ageing.

Memory is so important to our everyday functioning that permanent impairment of the processes can greatly damage the quality of our lives. The effects can range from the relatively mild damage from marijuana use to the highly debilitating symptoms of Alzheimer's disease. There are many sources of memory impairment and this chapter will introduce you to those that are most common, and those that have the most debilitating consequences.

Neurosis

Effects of neurosis
Sometimes an emotional trauma, or a threat to their ego integrity causes people to lose their memory. When this happens their

unconscious mind is protecting them from something they may not be able to cope with. This is known as hysterical amnesia, or fugue. Typically the sufferer will disappear from their present surroundings and relationships and find that they have to start a new life without memory of their past. In many cases the memory eventually returns.

Chemical abuse

Effects of drug abuse
Various kinds of drug abuse have effects upon the memory, some more serious than others.

Alcohol
Long-term alcohol abuse tends to result in a condition known as Korsakoff's syndrome. This is a form of encephalitis (brain inflammation) caused by vitamin B (Thiamin) deficiency. The result is severe and permanent damage to the hippocampus and mammillary bodies.

Effects of long-term use of illicit drugs
Long-term usage of marijuana causes deterioration of short-term memory. Other drugs also have a negative effect on memory.

The effects of LSD
LSD and other hallucinatory drugs distort perception and therefore distort storage. Involuntary recall of the material sometimes makes users relive experiences which did not really happen, at least in the form they are relived. These occurrences are known as flashbacks. These recalls are then re-stored making the false memory even stronger.

Effect of carbon monoxide
Carbon monoxide poisoning affects the memory. It causes retrograde amnesia, i.e. it affects memory of events prior to the illness.

Physical illness

Memory deficits due to viral infection

Viral infection can affect the brain and damage the memory. In a famous case of extreme damage in this respect a patient called Clive Wearing suffered brain damage as a result of the normally relatively harmless condition known as *herpes simplex* – the common cold sore. His hippocampus was destroyed, along with other brain areas.

The main effect was that he was no longer able to transfer material from short-term memory to long-term memory. Consequently, from the illness onwards, he could only ever remember the last few minutes from the present moment. He was able to recall some parts of his life before the illness, but they were patchy.

He had been an accomplished musician before his illness and his ability in this respect remained intact. He was also able to learn new skills. This is commonly the case with amnesiacs; reflex memory, or memory for skill learning is usually resilient.

The effect of cardiovascular disease

Cardiovascular disease can affect memory in a number of ways, the most common being the effect of stroke. A stroke is a blockage of the blood supply in an area of the brain, which causes that area to die. Alternatively, it can take the form of a haemorrhage in the brain.

The type of memory affected will depend on the site at which the damage occurs. Because of the law of mass action, it is unlikely that the effect on recall of previously stored material will be severe, because storage of memories is not localised, but fragmented in various sites of the cerebrum. Reconstruction is therefore not dependent on all the fragments being accessible.

Trauma

Effects of trauma

Trauma to the brain can cause serious effects on memory. According to Lashley's Law of Mass Action it is not the site of damage that determines the amount of cognitive deficit, but the amount of damage. This is because in the case of memory, material is stored in a fragmented way in various sites of the brain. Consequently, if one site is damaged, enough material is likely to be available from other sites to reconstruct the memory required for recall.

Damage to some sites, however, does cause serious deficits. The hippocampus is one such site. There is a well-known case involving an epileptic, referred to in research papers simply as *HM*, for reasons of anonymity, who was treated by surgical removal of the hippocampus on both sides of his brain. The result was that his long-term memory and short-term memory remained intact, but he could not transfer material from short-term memory to long-term memory. After the operation he suffered a very debilitating and distressing kind of memory problem. Like Clive Wearing, he could only ever remember the last 15 seconds from the present moment.

Road traffic accidents

Head injuries from road traffic accidents are a common source of memory deficit. If the damage is not too serious the effect tends to be temporary, retrograde amnesia.

The memory tends to gradually return, in a graded way. Oldest memories usually return first before memories closer to the time of the accident. What does not return, however, is the memory of the last few moments before the accident. This is because the individual was deprived of the consolidation period.

Memory and aging

There is no doubt that memory quality declines with age. Some types of memory are affected more than others, e.g. memory for words. Some types are hardly affected at all, for example, retention of stories.

Can we do anything about it?

Clearly it is possible to shore up aging effects in particular types of memory ability by learning memory techniques. Furthermore, since it is known which types of memory are affected least and which types of memory are affected most we can utilise the aging memory's strengths to shore up its weaknesses. Readers can obtain a comprehensive coverage of mnemonic techniques from my books *Improving Your Memory: McAndler's Unique 5 x 5 System,* and *Maximising Your Memory* (see Further Reading).

Although actual memory quality declines with age, a highly powerful and useful schemata-based memory quality goes on increasing throughout life. This is highly useful because it can also be thought of as crystallised intelligence, a kind of intelligence which is based on lessons from the past, rather than quickness of thinking.

Tutorial

Seminar discussion
Consider some of the practices which threaten our memory quality. Do we take the threats seriously enough?

Student assignment
Take any one of the memory impairment illnesses mentioned in this chapter and collect as much information as you can from such things as news reports, leaflets, fact sheets from relevant charities, internet sites, case studies and so on. Compile a project folder.

Practice questions
1. Which one of the following is correct? Hippocampal damage results in:

   a. long-term memory loss
   b. short-term memory loss
   c. memory consolidation failures
   d. brain death
   e. reflex memory loss.

2. Which one of the following is correct? In cases of amnesia:

   a. newest memories return first
   b. oldest memories return first

c. both old and new memories return at the same time
d. in most cases neither new nor old memories ever return
e. the order in which memories return cannot be predicted.

3. Which two of the following are incorrect? The amount of memory impairment as a result of brain damage:

a. depends on the amount of damage
b. depends on the site of the brain damage
c. is not related to the amount or site of damage.

4. How many of the following are correct? Korsakoff's syndrome:

a. is caused directly by alcohol
b. is a condition in which the memory is impaired
c. is caused by a vitamin deficiency
d. results in permanent damage
e. affects the hippocampus and mammillary bodies.

5. Which two of the following are incorrect? Cardiovascular disease:

a. only affects the blood vessels in the brain
b. can damage the memory
c. is another name for stroke or haemorrhage
d. has effects on the memory that are always irretrievable
e. results in cell death.

9

Individual Differences of Memory

One-minute summary: There appear to be individual differences in memory quality. To understand this we must distinguish between natural memory quality and trained memory quality. Both qualities, in various types of memory, can be measured.

In this chapter you will learn about:

▶ mnemonic-based memory quality
▶ the psychometry (measurement) of memory
▶ natural memory quality
▶ mono-savants.

Are there individual differences in memory quality among people? It seems there are. To understand the situation, however, we first have to distinguish between natural memory quality and mnemonic-based memory quality.

Mnemonic-based memory quality

More or less anyone can develop a high level of mnemonic-based memory quality. Its level is dependent upon the effort you put in to train your memory. Some of the most outstanding mnemonists in the world have average level natural memory quality and, in some aspects, many of them are even below average. Indeed memory training is the great intellectual leveller, for a highly powerful and useful kind of intelligence known as crystallised intelligence, can be developed by anybody regardless of their natural memory quality and, barring extreme cases, regardless of their IQ.[1]

Natural memory quality

Natural memory quality is a different thing. Some people are able to store and recall a variety of types of material in great quantity without use of any techniques. Such people invariably tend to report that they have a close relative who also has a superior memory. They also tend to report that they have very vivid imaging ability.

Mono-savants

Then there is a third category of superior memory performer. These are known as mono-savants, because rote memorising is their one and only ability. These people tend to have very low IQ levels. This ability tends to manifest itself where such an individual can play a piano tune after hearing it only once. They are not capable of explaining how they do it and are unlikely to have any idea themselves.

The psychometry of memory

Can natural memory quality be tested? It is indeed possible to test natural memory quality. In a study in which I was involved, a battery of tests[2] was used to test four samples of people for natural memory quality. The findings were factor analysed and a centroid factor was discovered. All the various tests of memory which were carried out, with the exception of face recognition, loaded on the centroid factor. The memory types tested were as follows:

► memory for structured pictures
► recognition of faces
► memory for words
► memory for name, face, number combinations
► everyday memory
► spatial memory
► memory for temporal ordering of pictures
► memory retention over time.

Distinguishing immediate memory, retention and recognition

Other distinctions we have to make are between immediate memory and retention, and between these two and recognition. They are all different processes.

Testing retention

To test retention, tests were repeated a week later.

Recognition

Tests of recognition of faces were also repeated a week later.

Deducting the effect of mnemonic-based memory quality

Most people use mnemonics to some degree. Relatively few people use any kind of advanced systems, but many will use things like *one is a bun, two is a show, three is a tree* and sayings like *Richard of York gave battle in vain,* to remember things like the colours of the rainbow. It could be expected, therefore, that regardless of what the test subjects claimed to the contrary, they may well have been using some mnemonic skills at least some of the time. It was necessary to be able to deduct the effects of any such skill usage. The way this was achieved was by designing two tests for each type of memory tested. In each case one such test lent itself well to memory techniques and the other did not. An example of this distinction is in the testing of memory for pictures. One test employed pictures of snowflakes. It is very difficult to use any kind of mnemonic device to memorise the shapes of individual snowflakes. The second test employed a geometric structure of lines and other shapes, which could easily be associated with any number of objects in the minds of the test subjects. By deducting the scores of the first test from the scores of the second test the effect due to mnemonic skill usage could be ruled out.

Tutorial

Seminar discussion

Consider the utilities of measuring memory quality in individuals.

Student assignment

Select a sample of a dozen people. Download the list of words and the list of nonsense syllables from *thememorysite.co.uk*

Ask the people in your sample to spend 4 minutes memorising the list of words. Test each of them after a further one minute and score the results.

Repeat the process using the nonsense syllables.

Compare the scores of each subject for both the words and the nonsense syllables. Is the score order the same? If not, why might this be the case.

Deduct the nonsense syllable score for each subject from their word recall score. What do the differences suggest to you?

Practice questions

1. Which of the following is correct?

    a. to have a good memory you have to have a high IQ
    b. IQ and memory quality are inversely proportional
    c. there is a small association between natural memory quality and IQ
    d. there is no relationship between memory quality and IQ
    e. People with high IQ have a high natural quality and a low trained memory quality.

2. Which of the following is true? People with high natural memory quality usually:

    a. think without images
    b. are usually unique in their family
    c. have vivid imagery ability
    d. are likely to have a close relative with a superior natural memory
    e. tend to naturally use memory techniques.

3. Select the most correct answer. To measure natural memory quality you have to:

    a. add the scores from technique-friendly tests and technique-unfriendly tests.
    b. use only technique-unfriendly tests

c. use natural memory tests
d. deduct the scores of the technique-unfriendly tests from those of the technique-friendly tests
e. deduct the scores of the technique-friendly tests from those of the technique-unfriendly tests.

Bibliographical notes

1. Marshall, P. (1996)
2. Wilding, Valentine, Marshall and Cook (1999).

Glossary

Abreaction Releasing the power of repressed memories.

Adapted child A memory store of tactics for gaining attention.

Admonishing parent That part of the superego which discourages, rather than encourages.

Articulatory loop That part of short-term memory which handles acoustically coded data.

Association Mentally linking one thing with another so that one serves as a cue for the other.

Autobiographical memory A memory store of past events.

Backward conditioning Classical conditioning where the unconditioned stimulus comes second.

Central executive control The internal controller of short-term memory.

Cerebellum The rear-most part of the brain. It is concerned mainly with reflex memory.

Cerebrum The top layer of the brain. There are two lobes, each consisting of large folded layers.

Chaining Linking associations together to remember information in a series.

Chunking Grouping material prior to storage to optimise the power of short-term memory, which can handle only 5–9 bits of information.

Classical conditioning An unconscious memory process whereby the nervous system learns to produce a response to an object or event which though not itself rewarding is related to something else which is rewarding. It happens when the individual is exposed to the rewarding stimulus and the non-rewarding stimulus within fifteen seconds of each other. Just as it works with rewarding stimuli, so it also applies to threatening stimuli.

Conditioned response The learned response to the non-directly rewarding stimuli in classical conditioning.

Confabulation Unconsciously false recollection.

Context-dependent memory Material that can be recalled in the same context in which it was stored.

Cue (internal) Something internal which acts as an indirect stepping-stone to recall. It may be a mood or a feeling which was stored at the same time as something you want to remember.

Cue-dependent memory Material that can be recalled if an appropriate cue is given.

Declarative memory A store of knowledge.

Deletion One of the sources of distortion of perceived and stored material. We can only attend to a few features, because of the limits of our perceptual set, so we omit others. What we choose to attend to and what we choose to leave out will depend on our own perceptual set and the influence of others.

Dentate nucleus A small part of the cerebellum that influences motor and pre-motor responses.

Displacement Distorting recall of anxiety provoking material by focusing on something which is anxiety provoking at a lower level.

Distortion Altering what we perceive so that it fits in with our knowledge and understanding.

Dual process model A model of memory which posits that there are separate long-term and short-term memory processes.

Eidetic memory Photographic memory.

Fissure of Sylvius The cleft that separates the temporal lobe from the frontal lobe and parietal lobes of the brain.

Fixation Where part of an individual's psyche has remained in an earlier developmental stage. This tends to occur where conditions were too harsh to allow it to adequately satisfy its desires for the rewards available in this stage, or too comfortable for it to want to move on.

Flashback Spontaneous recurrence of a drug induced hallucination.

Flash bulb memory A memory store of very short duration (about a half second). It consists of chemical processes in the retina.

Forward conditioning Classical conditioning where the uncondi- tioned stimulus occurs first.

Free association techniques A technique used by Freud to hunt down repressed memories. Subjects would be asked to utter the stream of thoughts that came into their head. When the stream stopped abruptly it was assumed that a repressed memory was responsible.

Generalisation The natural process whereby a learned response to a particular object or event will make us produce a similar, if less intense, response to similar objects or events.

Granule cell A neuron whose cell resides in the granule layer of the brain.

Habituation A learned indifference to an object, condition, or event.

Hippocampus A structure in the temporal lobe that plays a crucial role in transfer of material from short-term memory into long-term memory.

Iconic memory A memory store of very short duration.

Implosion therapy A therapy that is like saturation therapy except that the subject is encouraged to imagine the phobia object, rather than being actually exposed to it.

Incidental storage Material that is unintentionally stored.

Law of reverse effect A natural tendency for our minds to do the opposite of what we want them to do. When you try hard to go to sleep, you just stay awake. If you, instead, try hard to stay awake you will go to sleep.

Level of processing model A model of memory, which provides that long and short-term memory are not separate processes. It is the level of processing that determines how long the memory will endure. There is good evidence challenging this model.

Limbic system Structures of the brain lying below the corpus callosum. The system includes the hippocampus, anterior thalamus, septum, amygdala and hypothalamus.

Long-term memory A memory store wherein memories can last a lifetime. Storage requires the material to first enter short-term memory and from there, if it is processed semantically, it will be stored in long-term memory. At the neurological level, long-term memory differs from short-term memory in that the former involves new protein growth.

Long-term potentiation The biological process underlying long-term memory.

Mammillary bodies Two small round structures in the medial thalamus thought to be involved in sexual and emotional behaviour.

Mnemonics Practical memory enhancement techniques.

Mossy fibre A kind of nerve fibre.

Motivated forgetting Recall failure which is purposive, i.e. it serves the purpose of protecting an individual from the anxiety which recall would cause.

Multi-store model A model of memory that assumes there are several different sub-systems in human memory.

Negative reinforcement Punishing particular behavioural responses.

Norepinephrine A catecholamine functioning as a neurotransmitter, synthesised in the locus ceruleus and in the post-ganglionic neurons of the sympathetic nervous system.

Nurturing parent That part of the super-ego which encourages rather than discourages.

Occipital lobe The posterior lobe of the cerebral hemispheres.

Oedipus complex A complex of inconsistencies to possess the opposite sex parent and eliminate the same sex parent.

Olfactory cortex The part of the brain dealing with the perception of smell.

Operant conditioning A form of learning whereby associations between particular behaviours and rewards, or escapes from punishment, are stored in reflex memory.

Phobia An accidental association stored in reflex memory, involving a harmless object, condition or event and frightening emotion.

Positive reinforcement Rewarding particular behavioural responses.

Prevention of consolidation Memories stored in long-term memory require a consolidation period to become permanent.

Primary acoustic store That part of short-term memory which temporarily stores material.

Primary visual cortex Part of the brain situated at the medial-caudate pole (middle section of the rearmost part) of the brain's occipital lobe.

Proactive interference Blocking of a memory by material stored before it.

Procedural memory An unconscious memory store of psychomotor skills.

Projection Shielding oneself from recall of shameful self-attribution, by assuming the qualities are present in another person.

Protein kinase An enzyme activated by the second messenger molecule cAMP, which phosphorylates and covelently changes certain target proteins in the process of long-term memory storage.

Recoding Changing the nature of a memory on storage, or on recall.

Recovered memory therapy A psychotherapy movement that has achieved considerable notoriety. Practitioners assume that neurosis is caused by repressed memories, principally of satanic ritual abuse or abduction by aliens, and guide their patients to remember such things.

Reflex memory Unconscious memory for reflex actions and responses.

Regression Where an individual copes with severe anxiety by regressing mentally to an earlier developmental stage, where such anxiety level was not present.

Reinforcement Rewarding or punishing particular behavioural responses.

Repression Burying anxiety-provoking memories or feelings out of reach in the unconscious mind.

Retroactive interference Blocking of a memory by material stored after it.

Saturation therapy An alternative approach to curing phobias by desensitisation. It is not systematic. The individual is exposed to the phobic object immediately so that the anxiety level reaches its ceiling. There is, then, only one way for it to go. Anxiety needs energy to fuel it; when it has reached maximum it will run out of energy and so the level will subside. As it does so, progressively lower levels of anxiety will be stored in relation to the stimulus.

Schemata A structuring of memories which updates itself from new storage and periodically restructures itself to maintain its consistency and equilibrium.

Self-esteem The difference between ideal self-concept and actual self-concept.

Seratonin 5-hydroxytryptamine (5HT) a neurotransmitter belonging to the 'indoles' group of compounds, synthesised in the brain stem.

Shaping Encouraging behavioural change by segmenting the undesired behaviour and rewarding any changes for the better.

Short-term memory A dynamic memory store wherein material is temporarily stored while it is being worked upon. It lasts only between 15 and 30 seconds, during which time it may or may not enter long-term memory.

Simultaneous conditioning Classical conditioning where both the unconditioned and the conditioned stimulus are presented simultaneously.

Somatosensory cortex The area of the brain lying as a vertical strip just behind the Fissure of Rolando, that processes sensory feedback from the body.

State-dependent memory Material that can be recalled if an individual is in the same mood as when the material was stored.

Superego A moral memory store in which, up to the age of five, a child stores uncritically the attitudes, values and rules of behaviours of its parents and other authority figures. It infers these from their direct relations with it and from what it witnesses in their responses to the behaviour of others.

Suppression Consciously blocking recall.

Systematic desensitisation: A means of curing phobias by systematically storing associations that contradict the association underlying the phobia. For example, if a person is afraid of spiders then the individual may be exposed to a rather unrealistic, and non-threatening, picture of a spider, while the anxiety it produces is compensated for by conditions which induce feelings of comfort and security. Gradually the level of the phobic stimulus is increased, all the time with compensatory stimuli to produce positive, anxiety-free responses. These positive responses are stored in association with the images of spiders and will serve to inhibit the phobic responses. The stimulus which is not itself rewarding, or threatening gains its power to stimulate by its contiguous relationship to the directly rewarding or threatening stimulus.

Thalamus The largest section of the diencephalon region of the brain. There are twin thalami connected through the third ventrical by tissue known as the massa intermedia. Together, the thalami work as a relay system (transferring sensory data except the olfactory data) to various parts of the brain.

Thorndyke's Law of Effect If behaviour is rewarded it will be repeated.

Trace decay Gradual atrophy of the neural changes that took place when something was stored in memory.

Unconditioned response The response to the directly rewarding, or threatening stimulus in classical conditioning

Unconditioned stimulus The directly rewarding, or threatening, stimulus in classical conditioning.

Areas V_1, V_2, etc. All areas referred to as 'V' + a subscript number are areas which process vision.

Visuo-spatial scratch pad That part of the short-term memory which handles spatial material.

Further Reading

Dr Peter Marshall's books are sold all over the world and have been translated into nine laguages. Here is a selection of some of his works.

Marshall, P. (1995) *Study & Learn*, 2nd edition, Oxford: How To Books
_____ (1997) *Research Methods*, Oxford: How to Books
_____ (1998) *Maximising Your Memory*, Oxford: How To Books
_____ (1999) *Unlocking Your Potential*, Oxford: How To Books
_____ (2000) *Human Memory on the Internet*, Plymouth: International Briefings
_____ (1999) *Studying Psychology*, Somerset: Studymates
_____ (2000) *Improving Your Memory: McAndler's Unique 5 x 5 System*, London: Guild Publications
_____ (2000) *Essentials for Remembering Names and Faces*, London: Guild Publications

Video
Improving your memory: McAndler's Unique 5x5 System, Oram-Juty

Research paper
Wilding, J., Valentine, E., Marshall, P. and Cook, S., 'Memory, IQ and examination performance', *Educational Psychology*, vol. 19, no. 2, 1999, 117–132

Useful web site addresses
http://ai.mit.edu/people/ekm/au
http://religioustolerance.org/rmttec.htm
http://psy.uq.edu.au/CogPsych/Noetica/OpenForumissue6/todam/TODAM.html
http://www.amzona.edu/~psych/tacdtis/vperi.html
http://www.dartmouth/edu/dms/ptsa/KQ_Spring_1996.html

www.soton.ac./uk/~psgweb/statpages/sust/tecl/html
www.dcn/davis.ca.us/btcarrot/skeptic/repressedmemory.html

Bibliography

Abernathy, E. M. (1940) 'The effects of changed environmental conditions upon the results of college examinations', *Journal of Psychology*, vol. 10, 293–301.

Adler, A. (1917) 'A study of organic inferiority and its psychological compensations: A contribution to clinical medicine', NY: *Nerv and Ment. Sis. Publ.*

Asch, S. E. (1951) 'Effects of group pressure upon the modification and distortion of judgments', in H. Guestzkow (ed.), *Groups, Leadership and Men*. Pittsburgh, Pen: Carnegie Press.

———— (1956) 'Studies of independence and submission to group pressure: A minority of one against a unanimous majority', *Psychological Monographs*, vol. 70(a) (Whole No. 416).

Atkinson, R. C. and Shiffrin, R. M. (1971) 'The control of short-term memory', *Scientific American*, vol. 224, 82–90.

Baddeley, A. D. (1986) *Working Memory*. Oxford: Oxford University Press.

———— (1990) *Human Memory*. Hove, E. Sussex: Lawrence Erlbaum.

———— (1996a) 'The influence of acoustic and semantic similarity on long-term memory for word sequence', *Quarterly Journal of Experimental Psychology*, vol. 18, 302–9.

———— (1996b) *Your Memory*. London: Prion.

Bahrick, H. P., Bahrick, P. O. and Wittlinger, R. P. (1975) 'Fifty years of memory for names and faces: a cross sectional approach', *Journal of Experimental Psychology*, General, vol. 104, 54–75.

Bahrick, P. and Phelps, E. (1987) 'Retention of Spanish vocabulary over eight years', *Journal of Experimental Psychology: Learning Memory and Cognition*, vol. 13, 344–9.

Bartlet (1932) *Remembering*. Cambridge: Cambridge University Press.

Bickford, R. G. *et al*. (1958) 'Changes in memory function produced by electrical stimulation of the temporal lobe in man', *Res. Publ.*

Assoc. Res. Nerv. Ment. Dis., vol. 36, 227–43.

Blakemore, C. (1988) *The Mind Machine*. London: BBC Publications.

Bloedel, J. R. *et al.* (1991), 'Substrates for motor learning. Does the cerebellum do it all?', *Ann. NY Academy of Science*, vol. 627, 305–18.

Bower, G. H. (1981) 'Mood and Memory', *American Psychologist*, vol. 36, 129–48.

Bransford, J. D. *et al.* (1979) 'Some general constraints on learning and memory research', in L. S. Cermack and F. I. M. Craik (eds) *Levels of Processing in Human Memory*. Hillsdale, NJ: Lawrence Erlbaum.

Craik, F. and Lockhart, E. (1975) 'Levels of processing', *Journal of Verbal Learning and Verbal Behaviour*, vol. 11, 671–84.

Craik, F. and Tulvin, E. (1975) 'Depth of processing and retention of words in episodic memory', *Journal of Experimental Psychology*, General, vol. 104, 269–94.

Collins, A. M. and Loftus E. F. (1975) 'A spreading activation theory of semantic processing', *Psychological Review*, vol. 82, 407–28.

Cohen, G. (1986) 'Everyday memory', in G. Cohen, M. W. Eysenck and M. E. Le Voi (eds) *Memory: A Cognitive Approach*. Milton Keynes: Open University Press.

_____ (1990) 'Memory', in J. Roth (ed.) *Introduction to Psychology*, vol. 2. Hove, E. Sussex: Lawrence Erlbaum.

Descartes, R. (1998) H. H. Joachim (ed.) *Rules for the Direction of Mind*. London: Thomemms.

Dollard, J. and Miller, N. E. (1950) *Personality and Psychotherapy*. NY: McGraw Hill.

Eich, J. E. (1980) 'The cue-dependent nature of state-dependent retrieval', *Memory and Cognition*, vol. 8, 157–73.

Eysenck, M. W. (1970) 'Depth, elaboration and distinctiveness', in L. S. Cermack and F. I. M. Craik (eds) *Levels of Processing in Human Memory*.

Eysenck, M. W. and Eysenck, A. C. (1980) 'Effects of processing depth, distinctiveness and word frequency on retention', *British Journal of Psychology*, vol. 71, 1980, 263–74.

Harris, T. (1970) *I'm OK – You're OK*. London: Pan.

Hull, C. L. (1943) *Principles of Behaviour*. NY: Appleton, Century Crofts.

Hunter, I. (1964) *Memory*. Harmondsworth: Penguin.

Jones, R. A. (1924) 'A laboratory study of fear. The case of Peter', *Pedagogical Seminary*, vol. 31, 308–15.

Kandell, R., Schwartz, J. H. and Jessell, T. M. (1991) *Principles of Neural Science*, (3rd edn.) London: Prentice Hall.

Lashley, K. (1929) *Brain Mechanisms and Intelligence: A quantitative study of injuries to the brain*. Chicago: University of Chicago Press.

Loftus, E. F. and Palmer, J. C. (1974) 'Reconstruction of automobile destruction: An example of the interaction between language and memory', *Journal of Verbal Learning and Verbal Behaviour*, vol. 13, 585–9.

McAndler, R. (1999) *Improving Your Memory*. London: Guild Publications.

Marshall, P. (1996) *Maximising Your Memory*. Oxford: How To Books.

Miller, G. A. (1956) 'The magical number seven plus or minus two: Some limits in our capacity for processing information', *Psychological Review*, vol. 63, 81–97.

Milner, B. (1996) 'Amnesia following operation on the temporal lobes', in C. W. M. Whitty and O. L. Zangwill (eds) *Amnesia*. London: Butterworths, 109–33.

Mowrer, O. H. (1950) *Learning Theory and Personality Dynamics*. NY: Ronald Press.

Neisser, U. (1982) *Memory Observed*. San Francisco: Freeman.

Penfield, W. (1958) 'Functional localisation in temporal and deep sylvian areas', *Res. Publ. Assoc. Res. Nerv. Ment. Dis.*, vol. 36, 210–26.

Salame, P. and Baddeley, A. D. (1982) 'Disruption of short-term memory by unattended speech: Implications for the structure of working memory', *Journal of Verbal Learning and Verbal Behaviour*, vol. 21, 150–64.

Schopenhauer, A. (1974) E. F. J. Payne (transl.) *The World as Will and Representation*, vol. 1. Dover Publications.

Thomson, R. F. (1988) 'The neural basis of basic associative learning of discrete behavioural responses', *Trends Neuroscience*, vol. 11, 152–5.

Treisman, A. and Gormican, S. (1988) 'Feature analysis in early vision. Evidence from Search Asymmetries', *Psychol. Rev.*, vol. 95, 125–48.

Triesman, A. (1988) 'Features and Objects', The Fourteenth Bartlett Memorial Lecture, *Q. I. Exp. Psychol.*, vol. 40A[2], 201–37.

Watson, J. B. and Raynor, R. (1920) 'Conditioned emotional reactions', *Journal of Educational Psychology*, vol. 3, 1–14.

Wilding, J. and Valentine, E. (1997) *Superior Memory*, Hove: Psychology Press.

Wilding, J., Valentine, E., Marshall, P. and Cook, S. (1999) 'Memory, IQ and exam performance', *Educational Psychology*, vol. 19, no. 2, 117–32.

Index